Contents

Foreword

YOUNG CHILDREN LEARNING MATHEMATICS is a collection of articles about the learning and teaching of mathematics with our youngest children. The articles making up this book were published in **Mathematics Teaching** during 2001 and 2002. All are original and related to the learning and teaching of mathematics with children aged between 3 and 7 years.

ATM is an *association* of teachers; we are all able to make a contribution to the craft of teaching. **Mathematics Teaching** articles do not represent an 'official' view on the teaching of mathematics, whatever that may be. Contributors are encouraged to express their personal views on the teaching and learning of mathematics. Within this collection you will find a range of views and opinions represented, touching on a wide range of issues; including a particularly timeless article first published in 1977 (Ken Saunders, *'Who is doing the thinking?'*, page 8) [1]. What all contributions have in common is that they are all primarily concerned with how I, as a teacher, interact with children, how I support children thinking and talking mathematically, and how I respond to what I see and hear. Articles that focus on how children learn raise issues that are relevant to all ages and stages of the learner.

ATM is proud of its tradition of encouraging reflection and discussion on current practice.

This is based on a longstanding belief that it is developing the habit of reflection on one's own practice that is the key to becoming an effective, questioning, continually developing, increasingly confident and articulate professional.

> **"There is only one instrument in research to find answers. One instrument. And that is to raise questions."**
> *Caleb Gattegno, talking to the ATM Easter Conference, 1988.*

When I was a young teacher I was set a particularly sobering task. I was asked to observe some children I knew well, engaged in being mathematicians - and to intervene as little as possible. To my horror, my resulting tape-recording of a group of my reception children working together demonstrated that my interventions were more frequent and more intrusive than I intended. How do we learn different patterns of behaviour? I started by talking to others about what I was doing and what I was seeing. In putting together this collection of articles, the editors hope there is something here that will stimulate discussions of this sort and be a means of encouraging reflection and discussion with colleagues on our practice. Reading accounts of what has happened in other classrooms, with other children can cause us to ask: *"I wonder what would happen if I tried that with **my** children?"* We hope you leave this book with some questions of your own.

As we begin the 21st century, there are many challenges. At times such as these, with the ever-increasing number of publications claiming to 'deliver' mathematics, many emanating from government bodies; alongside an ever-growing mound of top-down decrees; plus the pressures of too-frequent testing and the subsequent comparison of results, it is difficult to retain a sense of what is important. We must continue to question and critically judge both materials and dictats. The current national focus is on what we provide – the resources, the time we spend, the 'what' of teaching; this will pass. In time, our focus will move back to how children learn and to how we influence children's attitudes to learning through what we say and do. This collection contains glimpses of classroom action and discussions that help us reflect upon our own situations and form our own opinions; to speak out against what is inappropriate.

We must celebrate both the complexities of teaching and learning – we know there is no one strategy for teaching mathematics - and the excitement that is teaching. However familiar an activity might be to a teacher, different groups of children will always have the ability to cause surprise – we must leave space for this surprise to happen.

"I learnt it because I allowed my students to enlighten me."
Caleb Gattegno, talking to the ATM Easter Conference, 1988.

Finally, it is critical that we continue to recognise young children as powerful mathematical learners, learners who are entitled to teachers that recognise them as such, and who work at tuning in to how they think. The articles contained here are evidence of this.

The articles in this volume are organised under the following headings:

In the classroom

Something noticed. Arguably, all the articles could have come under this heading! These contain a description and analysis of a mathematical 'event' with some young children.

Using resources

These focus on using a particular resource to stimulate some mathematics.

Role-play

Role-play is a particularly effective context for developing some rich mathematical experiences. Here are descriptions of how we might use this.

Discussions on children's learning

A wide-ranging collection of discussions relating to the 'how' of the mathematics curriculum.

Helen Williams – MT Editor

In
the
classroom

"6 IS NOT ODD AND 13 IS" Jane Bovey and Barbara Allebone

It was during my final teaching practice in a Y1 class that I became interested in how mathematical language sometimes hindered children's understanding of new concepts. This was especially noticeable with 'the difference between' two numbers. Even children, who could solve subtraction in a variety of contexts, struggled with the new vocabulary and were unable to see 'the difference' as numerical. Background readings supported this, and examples of 'difference between' were frequently cited with children as old as nine (Pimm 1987). Within the framework of the *National Numeracy Strategy* this concept is introduced in Reception, and I was interested in why older children were still having difficulties.

The role of language in developing children's understanding of new concepts has been established by influential theorists such as Vygotsky (1986), Bruner (1960) and Wells (1986). Cockcroft (1982) goes on to claim that '*mathematics provides a means of communication which is powerful, concise and unambiguous*' (para. 3 p1). Many researchers have disputed this idea of unambiguous communication, highlighting the way many words carry more than one meaning. To most five-year-olds 'face' is a part of the body and not a part of a 3D shape. In fact, Bell listed 365 words in common use outside of mathematics (Orton 1987 p126). I have found it is words such as these, that children come across in everyday life first, that cause the most misunderstanding.

I was surprised at how many times 'difference between' was used as an example to illustrate the errors children make (Pimm 1987; Matthews 1980; Hughes 1986; Durkin & Shire 1991; Orton 1987; Mathematical Association 1987). It appears that this particular word causes more problems than many of the others. I would suggest that this could be due to the complexity of the concept itself and the fact that the vocabulary is introduced to such young children.

Extensive research by Martin Hughes (1986) showed the potential young children have for carrying out subtraction with concrete objects but the difficulties they encounter when faced with the same problems in the abstract. He concluded that 'Children need to develop links – *or ways of translating* – between this new language and their own concrete knowledge' (p.51). Thus, children need to make a connection between this disembedded mathematical thinking and their own understanding. These difficulties are even greater when the language has an 'everyday meaning' that is different from its mathematical meaning.

Children's conceptual understanding of 'the difference between' was first discussed by Matthews (1980). She suggested that it is the conceptual understanding of subtraction as 'difference between' rather than the vocabulary that causes most difficulties. This is not surprising when considering the steps involved. First children need to understand the cardinal aspect of number. They need to be able to compare two quantities to establish which is more or less. They then need to be able to use counting-on or take away strategies to calculate the numerical answer. They also need to understand, and be able to use, the appropriate vocabulary to interpret the question.

I carried out an activity to assess children's understanding and use of the vocabulary of 'difference between' with four middle ability children from Y1, Y3 and Y5. I started by asking some questions to assess children's understanding of the mathematical vocabulary. I then introduced a game involving two dice, where the children had to calculate the difference between the two numbers rolled. The activities were tape recorded to allow me to analyse the language used.

The Difference Game

The children used a great deal of mathematical language, focusing on the numbers and a comparison between them. As was to be expected, the comparative language used by year 1 was less sophisticated than that of Y5. For example, year 1 talked about 'higher or smaller', 'little or big',

'mathematics provides a means of communication which is powerful, concise and unambiguous' – Cockcroft

To most five-year-olds 'face' is a part of the body and not a part of a 3D shape.

Difference Between Game

Phoebe aged 5 years 8 months

The game

Take it in turns to roll the dice and find the difference between the numbers thrown on the dice. The person who has the highest number gets one point.

Interpretation

Phoebe decided how to score. She had previous experience of scoring for a game.

The first go, P identified that A had one more. She made a new column labelled difference in which she wrote 1. Next to it she wrote 'A one'. (A won).

After 4 turns, P decided to use a 12-sided dice and wrote, 'changed dice'.

such as "That's taller and that's smaller". Even at the very end of the game when asked the difference between the two scores, Jemma replied "Me and Ryan have got little numbers and them two have got big numbers." This suggests that they were interpreting 'difference' to mean what is different.

I would suggest that a child who doesn't understand 'the difference between' will hear "What's…one and six?". This would help explain the following exchange:

Jane: So Karen needs to work out what's the difference between one and six?

Karen: …Seven, I got seven.

With verbal support from me such as "How many more would you need to add on 1 to get to 6?" most children were then able to work out the difference between the two numbers. They used a range of strategies to do this. Karen carried out

Difference Squares

Amy, 7 years 9 months, year 3, started using random numbers, then became interested in seeing what would happen if she used 'times tables' She progressed from 3s to 12s.

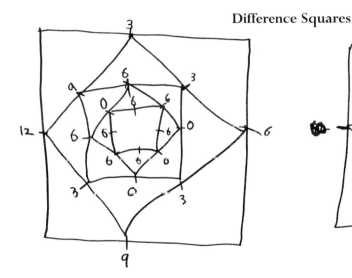

'bigger number' throughout, whereas as Y5 used 'more than' and quickly moved to discussing the value of the numbers themselves. This suggests that Y5 had a better understanding of 'the difference' as numerical rather than a comparison.

It is interesting to note that none of the children used the words 'difference between' despite having the opportunities to do so. In fact Maria (Y3) on rolling two dice to find the difference between, just asked "6 and 4. What's 6 and 4?" prompting Daniel to attempt to add them. This implies that the children were not confident using the vocabulary 'difference between' despite having been introduced to the concept and vocabulary in reception.

Y1

Y1 were shown two towers of multilink cubes which we counted. I then asked them what was the difference between the two numbers. Most of the children made visual comparisons with comments

mental take away sums. Ryan compared the two towers of multilink side by side to work out how many more would be needed to make the towers the same. David was able to use his fingers to work out how many needed to be added to 1 to get 6. Whereas Jemma, unable to make the numerical connections, was able to compare the two towers of multilink for size stating that "1 is smaller than 6".

To summarise, Y1 answers were often in the form of 'two more/less' indicating that they were still making visual comparisons.

Y3

It is interesting to note that Y3 were more confident when working mentally than with the dice, which could be due to the recent emphasis on mental calculations within the numeracy hour.

Initially their responses were based on visual differences such as

Amy: This one's smaller and this one's taller.

Jane: So, what's the difference between 12 and 18?
Amy: 12 is lower than 18

Jo: One's higher and one's lower.

However, with verbal support as given to year 1, they showed a basic conceptual understanding and were able to offer numerical answers. Their answers were often in the form of a comparison such as '6 more', '1 more'.

At times their lack of understanding of the vocabulary prevented them from understanding the numerical concept. This is demonstrated very clearly by the following exchanges:

Jane: So, what's the difference between 12 and 18?
Amy: 12 is lower than 18

Jane: What's the difference between 6 and 4?
Maria: Er....6 and 4, 6 and 4, 6 and 4, 6 and 4...6 is bigger than 4

Jane: What's the difference between 6 and 4?
Daniel: 6..6..7..no...5...6..7..8..8..

Y5

James's answer to "What is the difference between 6 and 13?" was "6 is not odd and 13 is". To me, this indicated he was interpreting difference in its everyday meaning. By Y5 I had expected the children to answer '7' as they have had plenty of experience of working out the mathematical difference between two numbers. Molly's response also showed what was different; "13 has got two numbers in it and 6 has just got 1." However, after the meaning of 'difference between' had been explained, Y5 appeared to understand 'difference between', giving numerical answers rather than comparisons.

Jane: What about the difference between 13 and 21?
Sophie: 8

Jane: What about the difference between 52 and 43?
Ben: ...9

However, none of the children used the term 'difference between' indicating they were not confident using the language.

All children initially responded to 'What's the difference between...?' by comparing the two numbers visually. It is possible that the use of the towers of multilinks with year 1 prompted this type of answer and it would be interesting to see if these children had more success when presented with countable objects, rather than a tower. However, the fact that even the children in Y5, who did not need the support of multilink, answered in a similar fashion suggests that they were interpreting 'the difference' to mean 'different'. This was further reinforced by the fact that none of the children used the vocabulary of 'the difference between' when discussing the problems with each other.

The way forward

My observations suggest that children as young as 5 are not conceptually ready for 'the difference between two numbers'. They are still developing many of the necessary mathematical skills such as comparing two numbers for more and less, and do not understand the ambiguous language. A recent report carried out by OFSTED (2000) has shown one of the weaknesses of the implementation of the numeracy strategy is 'Using equivalent words, such as minus and difference, for the four operations' (In Y3). I would suggest that delaying the introduction of this complex concept until children have a solid understanding of the processes of subtraction would help eliminate some of these problems.

How and when new vocabulary is introduced is therefore an important consideration. The *National Numeracy Strategy* draws our attention to this by producing lists of words to be introduced in each year group. Mathematical discussions are becoming a big part of the lesson and children are encouraged to use the new vocabulary. Straker (1993) recommends starting with the children's own natural language and negotiating a shared understanding of mathematical terms. In the case of 'the difference between' this means starting with the child's interpretation of what appears different and working towards a numerical answer. We also need to consider how we present problems involving the 'difference between' to allow children to interpret it in its mathematical sense. This is not an easy task as 'the difference between' belongs to that realm of mathematical language that has little meaning in the real world of 5- and 6-year-olds.

In nursery and reception we introduce the idea of 'different' by comparing sizes, shapes and colours and describing visual differences. In fact, we will often ask questions such as 'What is the difference between this square and this circle?'. Children become used to giving non-numerical answers based on what appears different, and it is no surprise that they respond to questions such as 'What is the difference between three and six?' in a similar fashion. Therefore we need to be aware of our own use of the word 'difference' to ensure that children see it as a numerical concept not just a visual difference.

Jane Bovey is a year 1 teacher at Warren Road Primary School and Barbara Allebone is a lecturer in primary maths at Goldsmiths, University of London

Bibliography

ATM (1993) *Talking maths, talking languages,* ATM

J.S. Bruner, (1960) *The process of education,* Harvard University Press

W.H. Cockcroft, (1982) *Mathematics counts,* Her Majesty's Stationery Office

DfEE, (1999) *The National Numeracy Strategy,* DfEE

K. Durkin, & B. Shire, (1991) *Language in mathematical education,* Open University Press

M. Hughes, (1986) *Children and number*, Blackwell

Mathematical Association, (1987) *Maths talk*, Stanley Thorne (Publishers) Ltd.

J. Matthews, (1980) "'Five more pages fewer'" in *Mathematics in Schools* Vol.9, No.3

OFSTED (2000) *The National Numeracy Strategy: an interim evaluation by HMI,* OFSTED

A. Orton, (1987) *Learning mathematics,* Cassell Education

D. Pimm, (1987) *Speaking mathematically*, Routledge & Kegan Paul

A. Straker, (1993) *Talking points in mathematics*, Cambridge University Press

L.S. Vygotsky, (1986) *Thought and language*, MIT Press

G. Wells, (1986) *The meaning makers*, Hodder & Stoughton

HOW MANY SNOW PEOPLE? Penny Latham

Between 1986 and 1989 a group of teachers met regularly at Abbey Wood Mathematics Centre, London, as a group affiliated to PrIME [1] in order to look at mathematical processes. The following description of a lesson with a group of seven Y2 pupils was one of the contributions.

It was near to the end of the Christmas term, and the children were given blank outlines of snow people, and some gummed paper hats, scarves and belts, and pairs of buttons.

I explained the way the snow people could be made different from each other by including, or not including, each of the four items. When Asif asked if it would be different if one snow person had the scarf round its head instead of its neck, we agreed that it would still be a scarf, and it was whether the scarf was there or not that was important. [2]

The children worked on their own, talking to one another about what they were doing, but without influencing each other, and produced many different snow people with apparent ease.

I suggested that we collected a set of snow people on the wall from those they had made. Each child in turn contributed a snow person that was different from those we had already collected. Everybody checked each time to make sure it was a new one, without any help from me. Eventually we collected 15 different snow people, and they all checked that they didn't have any more. [3]

I asked if they thought that any more were possible. After some thought, some suggested that there weren't any more. I asked them how they knew. They said it was because they couldn't think of any more. I said I wasn't really convinced by that argument, that just because they couldn't think of any more that there weren't any other possibilities.

I asked how we could find out if we had them all. What could we do to see that we had all the possibilities?

After some discussion, I asked the children how,

> I said I wasn't really convinced by that argument, that just because they couldn't think of any more that there weren't any other possibilities.

> Joe said that he had been looking first at all the different ones he could make with one item.

when they were working, they had decided which new snow people to make next. Joe said that he had been looking first at all the different ones he could make with one item. I stopped him and said that was interesting, and perhaps we could try that, and see if we had all of them with just one item. [4]

The children thought that was a good idea, so following their instructions I made a row of snow people, each wearing only one item. I asked if we had all the possibilities. Several explained that we did, because we had used each item, and there was nothing else to use. [5]

I asked what we were going to look for next. Joe suggested snow people with two things on. [6] The rest agreed, and we made a row of those underneath the other row. I asked again if we had all the possibilities, and they said we had, because you couldn't put any of the things with something different; for instance, we already had the hat with each of the other three things. [7]

I asked what next, and they were all clear that we would now collect snow people with three things on, so we made a row of those. I asked if there were any others to go in that row. Natasha quickly said there was another one. I asked what it would be, and she described exactly the snow person that was missing. I asked the others what they thought of Natasha's suggestion. They agreed with it, and Natasha made it and added it to the row.

I asked what we should do next, and they said there was only one to go in the next row, the one that had everything on.

We were left with the snow person with no bits stuck to it. I asked where this should go, and they said at the top, because nothing came before one thing. [8]

We now had a pattern of snow people.

Jack now said he could see a pattern. If you drew a line through the middle of the snow people that had three things, it would be a symmetrical

Tamaris Taylor

pattern, not, he said, in what the snow people were wearing, or in their shape, but in the numbers of snow people in the rows.

I asked if the others knew what 'symmetrical' meant. Aurelie was not sure, so I asked Jack to explain. He said it would be like having a mirror along the middle, and the pattern on one side was the same as the pattern on the other side. [9] The others agreed that this was so.

Jack then said there were 16 snow people, and the others seemed sure that there were no more. I asked how they knew that. Aurelie said it was because they had sorted them out, and so we knew we had them all.

Then Jack said again that there were 16 snow people altogether, and 16 was a square number, and you made it by 'timesing' 4 by 4, and there were 4 different things we had used to make these snow

people. He thought that was how he knew there should be 16. [10] I said to them that that was an interesting theory.

Jack went on to say that the 'next one down' would be 9, because you would use 3 things to make the different snow people, and 3 threes were 9. He talked his way back to one thing, and said if you had only one thing, you would only be able to make one snow person because one times one is one. [11]

Asif immediately said this was wrong. You could make 2, he said, because you could have one snow person with the thing on, and then another snow person with nothing on. [12]

Jack thought, and said he wouldn't include the snow person with nothing on. I asked if we had included the snow person with nothing on in our set. The children said yes. I put my hand over it, and asked how many snow people we would have if it wasn't there. Fifteen, they said. I asked if 15 was a square number. Adam said yes, because you could arrange it in rows of 5. Jack said it wouldn't be square, because you would have 3 rows of 5. Adam then agreed it would be a rectangle and not a square.

But the children still wanted to explore Jack's idea that three things would produce nine different snow people.

Penny Latham was a primary advisory teacher when this article was written, but now works as a freelance mathematics consultant.

Footnotes

1 Primary Initiatives i[n] Mathematical Education, a nation[al] project looking at t[he] primary mathemati[cs] curriculum which r[an] from 1985 to 1989 was based at Homerton College, Cambridge

2 Decision making is [an] important mathema[ti]cal process. Asif wa[s] asking for clarificati[on] about what he saw a[s] an ambiguity, and h[e] through discussion [...] helped to make a decision.

3 This sort of checki[ng] for duplicates and omissions requires [a] degree of organisati[on].

4 One way of organisi[ng] the check is to brea[k] the problem down i[nto] sub-problems.

5 A simple proof.

6 Another simple idea[,] but it is important t[o] put things into a log[ical] order.

7 Proof again, but a li[ttle] more sophisticated.

8 Another manifestati[on] of the principle of putting things in or[der].

9 Jack is pattern spotting, but in a fa[irly] sophisticated way, a[s] he is able to give a clear explanation of what he sees.

10 Jack has a hypothesi[s].

11 The hypothesis is generalised.

12 The hypothesis is tested and disprove[d].

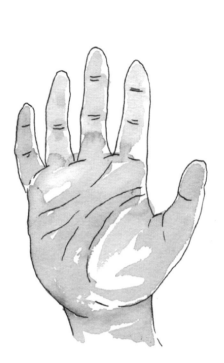
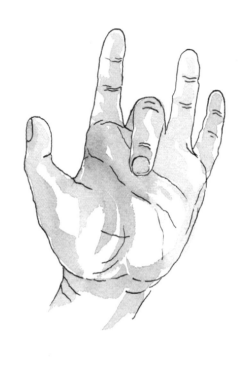
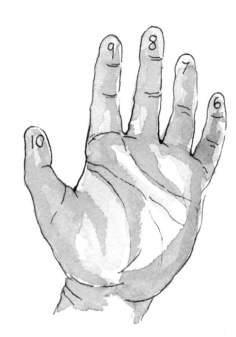

FINGER MATHS

Jeanette Harrison and Matt Strevens

One of the main aims of the national numeracy strategy is to enable all children to become numerate. Amongst other things, a numerate child at primary school . . .

- has a sense of the size of a number
- knows where numbers fit in the number system
- knows by heart multiplication and other number facts
- uses what they know to work out things in their head
- uses a range of methods of calculating, mentally and on paper

One of the biggest tell-tale signs for us in spotting key stage 2 children who have not attained such proficiency, is when they tackle calculations such as 36 + 12 by counting on in ones on their fingers. To discourage children from using their fingers in these situations we say, 'Use the facts that you know', or, 'Think what strategy would be useful for this calculation'.

We also recognise that including a kinæsthetic approach in our teaching helps children to become engaged in tasks, and helps them develop ways to consolidate understanding and to remember facts.

Taking both of these points on board, we set about trialing some ideas which built in using fingers to help children to develop a proficiency and confidence to work with numbers in their head. The following commentary outlines some of our observations.

Visualising fingers in a reception class

This was an activity taken from the Beam publication *Eyes closed* [1]. Half the class were asked to close their eyes, and whilst keeping their eyes closed hold up a stated number of fingers eg, 5. The rest of the class checked that the number of fingers were correct. I was amazed at how challenging the children found it to count their fingers whilst not being able to see them. It was a good opportunity to assess

I was amazed at how challenging the children found it to count their fingers whilst not being able to see them.

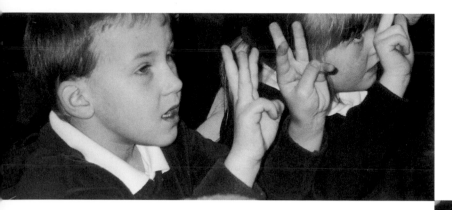

Tamaris Taylor

children who had mastered the skill of counting things that could not be seen. Also for numbers such as 5 and 10, to note the children who still needed to put up one finger at a time and those that knew to hold up a whole hand.

Checking answers in a Y1 class

The children were presented with a number sentence such as 5 + 1 = 4, and were asked to decide if it was correct or incorrect, and respond by showing yes/no cards followed by an explanation of why. Since the children had been working on addition and subtraction facts to 5, and adding 5 and a bit, the questions were selected to encourage them to demonstrate how well they had mastered such facts and skills.

Whilst they were taking a few minutes to share their answers with the person next to them, I observed a girl explaining with her fingers why 5 (holding up her hand), and 1 more, (showing 1 finger from her other hand) makes 6, and not 4. Because 5 (holding up her hand again) and 4, is one less than 5, (putting down one finger).

This was a particularly pleasing observation since she did not count out the five fingers each time, and was in effect using a known fact (the five in her hand) to work out new facts. She was using a kinæsthetic strategy to help justify her reasoning.

'Flashing fives' in Y2 class

After counting in hops of five on a large number line, the children were asked to watch as I flashed five fingers at a time, and count in their heads how many fingers I flashed at them. They responded by

showing their answer on petal cards. The two stages to the activity were intended to move their thinking from the visual number line, to mental pattern of counting in fives.

Next, the children worked in pairs, one flashing fives and the other counting and showing the answer with a petal card. The level of pupil involvement by now was incredibly high, and all children were successfully imagining the sequence of fives.

Now, the foundations were set for work on developing an understanding of multiplication. Questions such as, 'How many fives did I flash? So how many is that altogether?' followed naturally.

Using fingers to help work out multiplication facts for six to ten times tables – an individual challenge for a Y5 child

We decided to teach one child a kinæsthetic strategy for calculating multiplication facts. First, the fingers on each hand were labelled from 6 to 10, then selected fingers were touched together eg, 8 and 10, and a strategy for calculating 8×10 was taught [2]. The child was then asked to teach this strategy to another child.

It soon became obvious that the technique required the child to have two very important prerequisite skills:

- a secure knowledge of multiplication facts to 4×4,
- the ability to hold a two step calculation in their heads, eg, 20 + (4×4).

Although rather confusing at first, and not linked to any real understanding of number, I feel that with time given at the appropriate time to mastering the technique, it could become useful in helping derive those multiplication facts not known by heart. Like all mental strategies, it would need frequent use in order that it is not forgotten. Finally, it should be seen as one strategy within a wide repertoire from which children choose the most appropriate for any given calculation.

Jeanette Harrison is a numeracy consultant in Cornwall. Matt Strevens teaches at Treyew School, Truro.

References

1 Tom O'Brien, *Eyes closed*, BEAM, 1998 BEAM orderline: 020 7684 3330

2 This strategy is that referred to as 'A handy way for multiplying from 6 through to 10' in the adjacent article by John Dabell, *Mathematics at our fingertips.*

WHO IS DOING THE THINKING? Ken Saunders

This is an extract from Ken Saunders' M. Ed thesis first published in the ATM publication Recognitions, *No. 8, Jan 1977.*

A group of six- and seven-year-olds have just been told a story where all the rulers in the world have been destroyed (they have been burnt in a cauldron). KS, who, as part of the story, is chief of an island has called them together to give them the job of making some more rulers. Now, how do they intend to go about it?

Rodney: Get a piece of wood and a pen and write numbers. Then get . . . get . . . get a pencil and make little marks; straight ones, and when you've done five, make another big one.

Sandra: I would say you had a long bit of wood, then you mark it and it was as wide as an inch then you mark a . . . it out 'till you had twelve inches and then if it was too long cut a bit off the end and then . . .

KS: Yes, OK. Any other ideas?

Jon: If you have a long piece of wood then you mark it and it was as wide as an inch then you mark a...it out till you had twelve inches and then if it was too long cut a bit off the end and then . . .

KS: Can I stop you a minute, because all the inches have gone; they have all been turned into smoke!

Jon: Oh yeah! . . . Oh well . . . has . . .

Sandra: Metres!

KS: There aren't any metres either. They have all gone.

Jon: Then . . . if you knew how big an inch was . . .

Eliz: Say if you didn't know though?

Louise: I don't know how you would make a ruler.

I continue to act out my role as chief of the island and tell them that they have to make some rulers and the rulers have to work properly. I tell them that they can have strips of paper, felt pens, and anything else they want I will try to supply. (I had paper already cut into strips, but had, unfortunately cut all the strips the same length.) So they set about making rulers from the paper strips.

Sandra and Louise decide to work together, but the others worked individually. I am surprised at what they do. They all begin to make marks on a paper strip. The marks are very close together and every so often a longer mark is made. The response is the same with everyone, although there is no attempt to make the rulers the same. Rodney, who is rather impatient and likes to get a job finished quickly, makes his marks quite wide apart. He does put small marks between each pair of longer marks, but the longer marks are certainly not equally spaced, and he appears to make no attempt to do this, not even by eye. He puts some numbers on his ruler; roughly over each of the long marks, and numbers them from 1 to 12. Jonathan and Elizabeth do much the same, but their long marks are closer together, and Jonathan isn't too careful about the number of short marks between each pair of long marks.

Sandra and Louise have problems. They are working together, and have decided that one would start at one end of the strip, and the other at the other end. I guess they are going to have problems when they get to the middle, so I try to get them to think about what they are doing, as they seemed to be working independently.

KS: Is it important that all these marks are the same distance apart?

Sandra: No . . . I'm not putting them the same.

KS: It doesn't matter if some are wider apart than others?

Sandra & Louise: No...no.

I think they have misunderstood me, and think that I am referring to the lengths of the lines they are making.

KS: What I mean is . . . there, (pointing to the gap between two marks) do they all have to be the same across there?

Sandra: Oh, you mean . . . hmmm . . . wider?

KS: Yes.

Sandra: Oh!

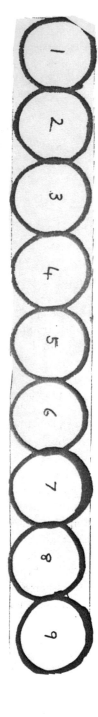

KS: Does it matter if some are wider than others?

Sandra & Louise: No.

Sandra: Yes . . . oh I don't know. Louise, do it like this and don't scrub . . . I'll have to go over all these . . . and don't press so hard.

Louise: Yours have got too many.

Sandra: It doesn't matter.

Louise: It does.

Sandra: Look Louise, when we meet up . . . say we meet there . . .

Louise: Oh, I've done it now . . . now I'll have to do all my numbers again.

The girls set about the task of putting marks on the strips by putting the long marks first, numbering these, and then putting in the small marks last of all. They are finding it rather tedious to put in so many marks so I say to them:

KS: If your ruler is too long you can cut it off.

Eliz: Yeah, I am. Can I cut it there?

Louise: Cut it there.

KS: Cut it where?

Louise: Cut it at nineteen.

KS: Nineteen? Is nineteen a good number to cut it on?

Sandra: No, no. I'm going to cut it there.

KS: What do you think would be a good number to cut it on?

Louise: Twenty-six.

Sandra: Twenty-nine.

KS: Why twenty-nine?

Sandra: Because if you see hm . . . well hm . . . well ha . . . I don't know. If you cut it at twenty-nine . . . I don't know what to say!

KS: Well, why did you say twenty-nine?

Sandra: Well, if you cut it on twenty-nine you see . . . you . . . you . . . you've only got one more to go and hm . . . you hm . . . and then you get another number.

KS: Thirty?

Sandra: Yes.

Eventually the rulers are finished and I explain that, in order to find out if the rulers work all right I want each of them to measure the length of the piano. Perhaps it was a mistake to ask them to measure something longer than their rulers, but I had in mind that out of this activity we might arrive at a good number at which to cut off the rulers. However, some interesting things happen when they measure the piano. Elizabeth measures it this way: She puts her ruler along the piano, puts a finger where the end comes, moves the ruler along to her finger and continues this process until she reaches the end of the piano. Then she simply reads off the number on the ruler which coincides with the end of the piano. In this case it comes exactly at the end of the ruler, so she says the piano's length is 29.

Sandra and Louise lay their ruler starting at one end of the piano. Realising that it is not long enough, they call for another ruler and borrow Rodney's. They place this end to end with theirs, but it still isn't long enough. They call for more rulers, and by the time they have Jonathan's and Sandra's they are just at the other end of the piano. I wonder how they are going to cope with the different rulers, for certainly Rodney's spaces are much wider than any of the others. But this is no problem, for they simply read the number off the last ruler which coincides with the end of the piano.

Jonathan is the only one who measures by laying his ruler repeatedly and counts the complete number of units.

When the measuring is completed, we sit around the table and I ask for the results. Of course, they are all different, ranging from 12 to Jonathan's 92. As chief of the island, I express some annoyance at this; so much so that I have to remind Louise that we are only pretending. We lay all the rulers on the table.

KS: Does anyone want to say anything about these rulers?

Jon: Well . . . not all the rulers are the same length. This one isn't the same length as this one.

KS: Does that matter?

Jon: Well this one couldn't be the same length as this one because this one is twenty-two inches and this one is only twelve.

Jonathan points to two rulers which are the same length but one was numbered to 22 and the other up to 12. I put these two rulers (Jonathan's and Rodney's) side-by-side and ask:

KS: Are both these rulers all right?

Rodney: No. I know why because mine's got five (pointing to the small marks in between the longer marks) and he's only got one, two, three, four . . . he's changed to three. (He has noticed that Jonathan hasn't been consistent with the number of small marks between each pair of long marks.)

KS: Well, what's wrong with all these rulers then?

Jon: Some rulers are different lengths.

Sandra: The rulers are different lengths.

KS: Well, why didn't you make them all the same length then?

Sandra: Well, because some of them were out there. (*The boys had been working in another room.*)

At the time of writing Ken Saunders was a lecturer in the mathematics department of St Luke's College, Exeter.

If you want to know what happens next visit the ATM website www.atm.org.uk and read the full story.

HANDSHAKES AND NUMBER BONDS: proof at Y1 Kath Halfpenny

After spending an exciting weekend with other maths teachers, organised by Geoff Faux and friends, to raise the profile of **proof**, I took away with me one dominating thought – to ask the question 'how do I know?' of the results of any maths work.

Dick Tahta had been unable to attend the weekend, but had sent some of his thoughts on proof. He states

". . . In any case I see two strands in any pedagogic discussion of proof.

● First in terms of collecting and illustrating ways in which mathematical deduction can be grasped and applied by children of any age.

● Second, in terms of clarifying why it might be useful and/or important to have this aim in the classroom . . ."

This, in turn, left me with two strands of thought to consider: I wanted to create opportunities for my pupils to use this process to access mathematical understanding. I also hoped that the very early foundations could be laid to enable my pupils to hang on to a process that could be applied in the future.

I feel we achieved this, particularly with the second activity.

Holding hands

I decided on two activities to explore these ideas. The first choice was to try to do something with the investigation on 'handshakes' (how many handshakes would be made with a given number of people). I decided to simplify it for my (young) class by investigating the possibilities when 4 people hold hands.

I approached this by demonstrating hand-holding very simply, using four children in a line. This gave us the answer three.

The children then tried for themselves, using five of our little people counters, finding the answer to be four. I then asked them how many they thought it would be for six people. Some were able to suggest an answer, and they all tried it out, again using apparatus. This exercised an approach that I thought would aid the next activity – of projecting an answer from a set of results. Some children then went on to explore the more complex investigation on 'handshakes'.

how many handshakes?

one	two	three	four	five
0	2	4	6	8

six	seven	eight	nine	ten
10	12	14	16	18

how many handshakes for 20 people? 38

how do you know? because we counted u- up in twos

Number bond symmetry

The next activity stemmed from the following Y1 national numeracy strategy learning objective: *know by heart all pairs of numbers with a total of ten.*

This activity led to a deeper investigation of the number bonds for other numbers and looking for patterns in the results. It drew on an activity that we had tackled earlier – the commutative law – ie, $2+8 = 8+2 = 10$. For some children the symmetry of the numbers seemed to help to consolidate the facts. I reminded the children of the work we had done, they therefore looked for each of what we called 'the partners' of the number bonds for 10. For each pair of numbers, eg, $3+7$, they knew that there would be the mirror pair ('the partners'), $7+3$. They found that there were eleven pairs:

$0+10$	$10+0$
$1+9$	$9+1$
$2+8$	$8+2$
$3+7$	$7+3$
$4+6$	$6+4$

$$5+5$$

The children found it amusing that $5+5$ did not have any 'partners' – was almost a palindrome. I have also found that if, when asking children if they remember the bonds to ten, the children who tend to be less confident in maths usually offer $5+5$ first. Is this because they remember doubles more easily? Or are they remembering it for its unique nature as a 'palindrome'?

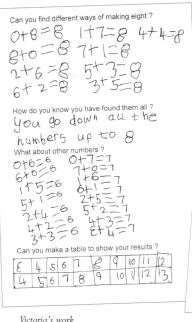

Can you find different ways of making eight ?

$0+8=8$ $1+7=8$ $4+4=8$
$8+0=8$ $7+1=8$
$2+6=8$ $5+3=8$
$6+2=8$ $3+5=8$

How do you know you have found them all ?

you go down all the numbers up to 8

What about other numbers ?

$0+6=6$ $0+7=7$
$6+0=6$ $7+0=7$
$1+5=6$ $1+6=7$
$5+1=6$ $6+1=7$
$2+4=6$ $2+5=7$
$4+2=6$ $5+2=7$
$3+3=6$ $4+3=7$
         $3+4=7$

Can you make a table to show your results ?

8	4	5	6	7	8	9	10	11	12
4	5	6	7	8	9	10	11	12	13

Victoria's work

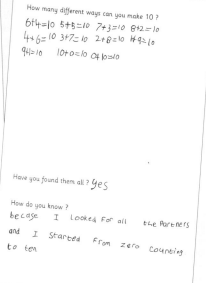

How many different ways can you make 10 ?

$6+4=10$ $5+5=10$ $7+3=10$ $8+2=10$
$4+6=10$ $3+7=10$ $2+8=10$ $1+9=10$
$9+1=10$ $10+0=10$ $0+10=10$

Have you found them all ? yes

How do you know ?

because I looked For all the Partners and I started From zero counting to ten

Stephen's work

Some of the children did take the investigation further. I asked all the children to investigate a given number on their own, using the same method as we had done for ten. I supplied the numbers, giving the less confident children smaller numbers, challenging the more able with larger ones. I then asked them to look at their results.

Victoria (Y1) and Stephen (Y2) enjoy maths and have shown good ability in the subject since they first joined our school. They both enjoy a challenge, particularly if it has an investigational slant. They both spotted a pattern. They established that where we had found eleven bonds for number ten, there were eight for number seven, and seven for number six – each time there was one more bond than the number under investigation. They were fascinated and highly amused by this.

When asking children if they remember the bonds to ten, the children who tend to be less confident in maths usually offer $5+5$ first. Is this because they remember doubles more easily? Or are they remembering it for its unique nature as a 'palindrome'?

For a small group of children, including Victoria and Stephen, who had not found the investigation too taxing, I asked them to use their results to estimate how many different bonds there would be for any number and then test their hypotheses. The table of results at the foot of Victoria's work shows their findings.

In the past I had attempted to assist children in their learning of the number bonds to ten using a variety of resources, including fingers, multilink cubes, 'ten in a bed' etc. We constructed towers of ten multilink cubes, using only two colours, in as many different combinations as we could. Using fingers we would put up given numbers of fingers, then count how many were down – this would give us pairs of bonds to ten, ie, if four fingers are up, six fingers are down, $4+6=10$.

But this did not seem to help the children to remember them easily. What obstructed the learning was a system – a logical approach – a *reason* to know them. It is never easy to internalise information if a context has not been given, or there is lacking a motivation to find out. Making this an *investigational* activity – asking the questions 'have we found all the different ways?' and 'how do we know?', gave it more purpose.

The question 'have we found all the different ways?' encouraged the children to follow a logical approach. Victoria's work on the number bonds for eight illustrates this, as she has gone through all the numbers taking each number in turn, ensuring that she includes them all – 'exhaustion' – investigating all the possibilities.

The question 'how do we know?' consolidated the element of proof and made the activity into one of mathematical enquiry rather than merely another set of facts to learn. The children, therefore, gained ownership of that enquiry. This means that they could reproduce their findings on number bonds in the future, as they internalised their results in a way that attempting to memorise will not do. I am confident that they would also be able to draw on this experience by using the process for future mathematical enquiry.

Kath Halfpenny works with a Y1/Y2 class at High Hesket Primary School, Cumbria.

> What obstructed the learning was a system – a logical approach – a *reason* to know them.

Using resources

SERENDIPITY, AND A SPECIAL NEED Tony Wing

It was odd how the nation's favourite word came to me, just at the time I was looking for a way to describe a very happy accident in some work I'm currently undertaking. A number of us have been engaged for a few years now in a local infants school developing an approach to early arithmetic that exploits a high degree of visual imagery and structural apparatus. (Remember structural apparatus? It's that coloured stuff that used to be recommended to infants' teachers before we discovered that counting and using our fingers was the royal road to arithmetic . . .)

We have been very successful in teaching infants through our visual approach lately. For the last three years the children we teach have been developing a very strong self-confidence in their number work, and have also been doing very well in their SATs. (It is important that children do well in their SATs because if they do, their teachers are allowed to decide for themselves how to teach).

The serendipity was at work early. It happened, several years ago, that as I pondered the problem of addressing a mathematics National Curriculum that required teachers to develop mental approaches to calculations during the early years, I found myself reading Catherine Stern's **Children Discover Arithmetic** [1] – and in that book met a Gestalt inspired approach to early years work that offered many parallels to Gattegno's arguments for Cuisenaire rods [2]. Thoughts began to come together and we began developing an approach that incorporated insights from Stern, from Gattegno, and from much more recent work regarding both something called 'concept image' [3], and the importance of early counting [4].

The approach developed well – our children responded to the combination of Stern patterns, number lines, counting activities and Cuisenaire rods that we used to represent numbers, we continued to develop and refine a progression of useful activities, and we learned many new things

about children learning mathematics. (Because young children show their thinking in how they act with these materials, their thinking is usually far more accessible through their actions than it is though their verbal accounts.)

The really happy accident that has occurred recently however (and which is the inspiration behind this report) is that the mother of a ten-year-old child with Down syndrome began to use our materials and approach with her daughter, and quickly reported striking successes. And the more that we discover about what might be going on here, and with other children with Down syndrome, the more it seems that we may have accidentally hit upon an approach to number and arithmetic which suits these children particularly well.

A brief description of what we do may help to explain what we think might be going on, although it is important to stress that we have not yet begun collecting data on a large enough scale to assess how generalisable our local findings might be.

Our approach begins with children engaging in both counting activities and in much 'free' (and not so free) play with series of Stern-inspired coloured plastic 'patterns' [5] and sets of Cuisenaire rods. A large number line which associates a Stern pattern, a Cuisenaire rod, a word, and (a) numeral(s) with each of the first twenty-two or so positions on the line is prominent in the classroom from the beginning, and various other pieces of supporting equipment are permanently available for children to play with freely whenever the fancy takes them. Many collections of objects (shells, beads, conkers etc.) and containers are available, and labels for equipment always include numerals as well as names, eg, '4 pencils', '6 scissors', etc. A plentiful supply of plastic coloured pegs that are the right size to fit into the holes in the Stern patterns is available, as are 10×10 'peg-boards' and sets of 1×1, 2×2, 3×3, etc. up to 10×10cm 'trays' which

Remember structural apparatus? It's that coloured stuff that used to be recommended to infants' teachers before we discovered that counting and using our fingers was the royal road to arithmetic . . .

are around for children to fill up with Cuisenaire rods in whatever ways they wish. Simply covering the peg-board with Stern patterns (without leaving gaps) develops familiarity with these patterns most powerfully, as well as involving children in much thought and activity regarding their geometric transformations.

Once children have become familiar with all these objects they are increasingly given specific tasks to accomplish with the material. Simply counting, stories and songs involving counting, and counting collections feature prominently with anything and everything available in the classroom. The structural apparatus (Stern patterns, Cuisenaire) is utilised in encouraging children to order things, and of course the number line in the background presents an ever present model of an order which will become increasingly significant.

Gradually, activities aim towards children making connections between all these ordering experiences, objects and images, with a view to them developing rich and connected 'concept images' for each natural number up to (possibly) as

What are Cuisenaire rods, after all, if not empty number lines?

to show bonds for each number to ten, and of course, commutativity. Staircases are utilised also to study 'one-more', 'two-more' (augmentation) and 'one-fewer' etc. (reduction).

And numbers get bigger. A number line to 100, based on centimetre units and with coloured decades, is introduced. The cardinality of ever larger collections is arrived at through making more and more patterns, importantly through arriving at (say) seven 'tens' and six – and can you find 'seventy-six' on the number line? Cuisenaire rods may be laid end to end along the number line to effect additions. Thus is place value approached painlessly through grouping in tens, and a founding image for 'the empty number line' offered. (What are Cuisenaire rods, after all, if not empty number lines?) Later on, multiplication and division are addressed in similarly visual and enactive, tactile ways. Throughout all the activities there is continual reference and connection made to everyday world contexts; the children are continually encouraged to

much as 22 or 23. Their counting connects with their work with patterns and rods in order to associate with each number a Stern pattern, a Cuisenaire rod, a word, (a) numeral(s), a position on the number line, and a loose collection of that many objects. Importantly, whenever children count a collection of objects they are asked to see if they can find that number on the number line. Stern patterns and Cuisenaire rods begin to acquire number names.

Gently, children are drawn towards 'finding how many, *without* counting'. An important next step towards children seeing numbers as 'wholes' (6 as '6', and not, 'one-two-three-four-five-six') is made by encouraging children to make patterns, to impose order upon randomly arranged collections. A random array of (say) twelve pegs can be put on the peg-board, and children asked to say how many there are, without counting. The only way to solve this problem is to make a pattern (or patterns), and if you make Stern patterns it is then very easy to find the 'ten-and-a-two' pattern on the number line as 'twelve'.

Once children have begun to form these rich concept images the first approaches to arithmetic can be made, but again *without* counting. Stern patterns and Cuisenaire rods are combined (addition-aggregation) and compared (subtraction-difference) in order to effect the basic number bonds and decompositions. Stern patterns are partially covered to show 'take-away' (partition). Cuisenaire rods are 'staircased' within number trays

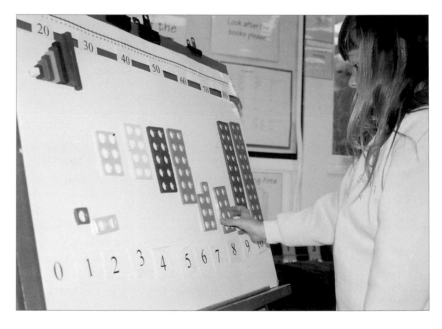

connect instances of everyday world 'mess' with the order of the number system through the making of patterns, the making of order in disorder.

Attempting an overall characterisation of our approach then, we seek to develop arithmetic understanding and competence through the use of visual and enactive experiences that emphasise the wholeness of numbers and their systematic interre-latedness (decompositions) in *patterns*. This stands in contrast to the orthodoxy enshrined within the National Numeracy Strategy *Framework* [6], in which children are expected to approach arithmetic through counting. We believe there is little virtue in

> Since we don't want them to count to do arithmetic when they're older, why do we praise them for doing it when they're younger?

References

1 C. Stern: *Children discover arithmetic*, Harper & Row, 1949

2 I have discussed this in MT157, Dec. 1996

3 S. Vinner: *The role of definitions in the teaching and learning of mathematics*, in D. Tall (ed): **Advanced mathematical thinking**, Kluwer, 1991

4 R. Gelman & C. R. Gallistel: **The child's understanding of number**, Harvard, 1978

5 These plastic materials have been produced variously over the years under the trade names *Triman* and *Multibond*. Currently they are produced under the name *Numicon* and may be purchased from Numicon Image Learning Systems Ltd., 12 b/c, Orleton Road, Ludlow Business Park, Ludlow, Shropshire SY8 1XF.

6 DfEE: **The National Numeracy Strategy Framework**, DfEE, 1999

7 J. Porter: *Learning to count: a difficult task?* in **Down syndrome research and practice**, Vol 6, No 2, August 1999

8 C. Gattegno, quoted in **A Gattegno anthology**, ATM, 1989

teaching children early methods of solving arithmetic problems which we will later want them to forget; since we don't want them to count to do arithmetic when they're older, why do we praise them for doing it when they're younger? (I know why we do, incidentally, and I think we're wrong; but that's another story and another article in progress.)

Returning now to the serendipity of a mother recently taking up our approach with her child with Down syndrome, it seems that children with Down syndrome typically experience a pattern of abilities and auditory disability which favours an approach to arithmetic through systematic visual and enactive imagery. Recent research by Jill Porter [7] points to specific difficulties children with Down syndrome experience in learning to count, and if counting is to be used as the basis of progression into arithmetic (as in the *Numeracy Framework*) these children will face their numerical future heavily handicapped indeed.

Jill Porter's research noted that children with Down syndrome offer a significantly different error profile to other children with severe learning difficulties, when learning to count. In particular, when learning to count collections of objects children with Down syndrome show a better grasp of one-one correspondence than of the stable order principle – put simply, they are better at matching words to objects than they are at consistently reproducing an ordered set of number names. To be even more specific, children with Down syndrome typically miss out number names when counting rather than recycling earlier parts of the number name sequence (as typically developing pre-school children do). This consistency in error pattern is the opposite to that shown by a matched group of children with other severe learning difficulties. And since the children with Down syndrome in the study had apparently developed the same size number vocabulary as the children with whom they were compared, their error pattern suggests they were probably having trouble forming appropriate 'next' connections between numbers – and this of course is a key barrier to progress with counting and an understanding of whole numbers.

To return to the success reported by the mother of a daughter with Down syndrome, it may be the case that the visual imagery and enactive experience involved in working with Stern patterns, Cuisenaire rods and number lines is offering this child an approach that addresses 'next' connections between numbers very powerfully, thus helping her to count. The two different kinds of 'staircase' that Stern patterns and Cuisenaire rods form when ordered do invite a visual/enactive perceptual association of 'one more' and 'next' that might be addressing

quite specifically a key difficulty. And of course in appealing to this child's visual and enactive experience anyway, we are appealing to her strengths, not to something crucially involving her impaired auditory discrimination.

It is possible too that there is a further gain in using Stern patterns and Cuisenaire at work here – that these approaches develop arithmetic *without* the difficult business of counting. In the case of Stern patterns it is the wholeness and interrelatedness of the patterns that take over from an understanding of numbers as 'the products of counting procedures', and with Cuisenaire it is the ungraduated continuity of each length. The opportunity to discover an arithmetic based upon an algebra of patterns and of lengths and not upon an elaborate counting apprenticeship might prove a particular further benefit to children with Down syndrome.

In our speculations about an as yet unexplained success with one child (although as I write considerable interest in our visual approach is being shown by many of those working with children with Down syndrome) we must obviously at this stage be careful about drawing any conclusions. We are currently preparing to undertake research into the progress made by a much larger sample of children. Yet we are minded to recall that we already have behind us considerable success with children in mainstream schools; and perhaps although children with Down syndrome undoubtedly experience particular difficulties associated with their condition, those difficulties may not be too far removed from those of anyone else trying to learn arithmetic.

In fact, it might be the case that the current orthodoxy of developing arithmetic through counting is an approach that faces every child with significant (and unnecessary?) difficulties. It might be worth recalling Gattegno's observation, during his final address to the ATM, that,

> ". . . counting is a complex activity. We have, for centuries, taught people, by offering counting as the basis of elementary arithmetic. It's wrong! Shall I say it louder? It's wrong. Not because I say so, but because counting is a complex activity. It's a complex activity asking of children more than is required in order to give them a better foundation." [8]

Maybe we have forgotten that?

Tony Wing is senior lecturer at the University of Brighton

The research reported here arose in collaborative work with Romey Tacon and Ruth Atkinson (Peacehaven Infants School) funded by TTA Teacher Research Grants 1996-8, and with Vikki Horner, Sue Buckley and Gillian Bird of the DownsEd Trust (Portsmouth). Development work is being undertaken in collaboration with all the aforementioned and with the Educational Psychology Service of Wiltshire.

FANTASTIC FROGS!

Kym Scott

Number rhymes can be used in many exciting and different ways to support the early learning goals for mathematics.

The rhyme 'five little speckled frogs' provided the theme for this display, which was set up in Lewisham's professional development centre. It provides a range of ideas, which would help develop young children's mathematical learning within the foundation stage.

Bringing the rhyme to life

Children can become familiar with the rhyme by:
- using frog puppets when singing the rhyme
- using magnetic props (made by laminating frog pictures and sticking magnetic tape on the back)
- making frog masks or hats to use when acting out the rhyme
- using real logs or tree stumps outside
- using plastic frogs, and a real log with a blue cloth or small tray of water as the pool, or in the sand/water tray

You could also make a 'five speckled frogs' number book using photographs of children involved in these activities or ask children to draw the frogs to illustrate a poster of the rhyme.

All of these experiences give children opportunities to practise counting, addition and subtraction in meaningful, exciting ways.

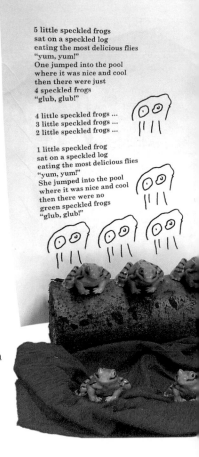

5 little speckled frogs
sat on a speckled log
eating the most delicious flies
"yum, yum!"
One jumped into the pool
where it was nice and cool
then there were just
4 speckled frogs
"glub, glub!"

4 little speckled frogs ...
3 little speckled frogs ...
2 little speckled frogs ...

1 little speckled frog
sat on a speckled log
eating the most delicious flies
"yum, yum!"
She jumped into the pool
where it was nice and cool
then there were no
green speckled frogs
"glub, glub!"

Beanbag frogs

Seeing how many beanbags they can throw onto a large lily pad provides children with a purposeful opportunity for counting, addition and recording numbers in the outdoor area. Children may record their score by:
- putting pebbles into a pot
- placing pictures of frogs onto a board
- drawing their own symbols
- using tally marks
- using numerals

Frogs in the box

This game uses plastic frog counters. Put different amounts into boxes with lids. Encourage children to shake the boxes and talk about how many might be inside. After they have checked the amounts, children can make labels to help them remember how many are in there. Children will soon be able to play this game on their own or with a friend.

How many frogs in the boxes? Write a number label for the box.

Throw the dice. Help the frogs get to their lily pads.

Frog race

Track games provide a fun way for children to practise using number names in order, and to link their counting with physical movements. This game could first be played on a large scale outside, with the children as frogs and the track chalked on the ground. A mini indoor version can easily be made by an adult and children can also make their own.

Sequencing and pattern

Plastic frog life cycle sets are useful for sequencing and ordering by size. Ordinal number labels can accompany these.

Many educational catalogues sell collections of frogs with different patterns, which can be used as discussion points as well as for sorting and matching activities.

There are a wide range of resources available based around plastic frog counters. These can be used for counting, pattern making, matching and sorting and activity cards are available with these.

1	2	3	4	5	6	7	8	9	10

Learning for life – a curriculum for the early years contains foundation stage information and advice across all areas of learning. It is published by Lewisham Early Years Service at a cost of £50. Telephone : 020 8695 9806

Kym Scott is an early years adviser for the London Borough of Lewisham.

DEVELOPING MATHEMATICS OUT-OF-DOORS

Judith Stevens and Kym Scott

It is important that practitioners plan for children's mathematical development out-of-doors. The outdoors provides a crucial background for exploring mathematical concepts which can be more easily understood if explored on a larger scale and linked to physical movement. The outdoor environment should complement and extend the indoor provision, rather than simply mirroring it. Therefore, it is essential that practitioners plan for activities that are enhanced by being outside.

It is useful to consider activities that:

- utilise the environment and natural objects
- are more effective on a large scale
- are noisy
- cannot be done easily indoors

The Curriculum guidance for the foundation stage [1] organises the thirteen early learning goals for mathematics into three separate aspects:

- Goals for numbers as labels and for counting
- Goals for calculating
- Goals for shape, space and measures

These ideas inter-link and overlap and many activities will involve aspects from several goals. For example, when using a tape measure, children will draw on their knowledge of number names, recognition of numerals and comparative language such as 'longer than' and 'shorter than' as well as calculating skills.

It is sometimes easy to overlook planning for shape, space and measures. Although much work at this stage will involve number, we need to aim for a balance across all areas of mathematics.

Children can work out-of-doors on a much larger scale. They will have opportunities for filling large containers with huge amounts and transporting large or heavy objects (including sand, gravel, natural objects and real bricks) using wheeled toys, wheelbarrows, trolleys or pulleys. A water butt or outdoor tap can be used to fill builders' buckets and paddling pools. Children can build with much larger items such as milk crates and empty cardboard boxes. Questions such as 'am I too big to fit in this box?' and 'how many children will fit in here?' can be answered after actually trying!

When children use outdoor climbing equipment, or make circuits of obstacle courses, adults can introduce and reinforce the use of mathematical language such as 'under', 'over' and 'through'

Large-scale playground games can be created to reinforce 2D shape names. Children and adults can

chalk shapes onto the floor and take turns in throwing a large shape dice or playing loud music and calling out shape names when the music stops.

Children can create patterns with a wide variety  of items including clothing hung onto washing lines. Patterns can be explored further as children chalk patterns on paving slabs. They can follow tracks, paths or routes chalked or painted onto the ground or made using movable dinosaur footprints. Children's outdoor play can be much louder than indoors and so there will be opportunities to use large-scale noisy instruments (steel drums or hanging saucepans) to follow, repeat or create sound patterns, perhaps developing a version of 'follow-the-leader'.

These activities can be developed so that children can follow a pattern of movements either verbally 'two jumps, three long strides, two jumps . . .' or from laminated cards with symbols to represent dinosaur steps, pigeon steps or hops.

The outdoor environment offers many opportunities for measuring,  particularly using non-standard measures: 'how many fir-cones long is this?', 'how many hand-prints tall are you?'. Large blocks can be used to measure the height of a playhouse.

Taking children on a number walk and taking photographs of the numbers seen in the local environment – on doors, signs, post-boxes and car registration plates can help them to see some of the ways in which numbers are used. A display, book or matching game can be made from photographs taken on the walk.

Numerals should be an integral part of the outdoor learning environment. This could include

weaving numerals into fencing, hanging numbered tee-shirts on a washing line, or making larger scale versions of number lines that are used indoors. Laminated photographs of children can be labelled to make an interesting and meaningful outdoor number line.

Parking bays made using chalked numerals or printed cards will encourage children to involve number in their play with wheeled toys. The vehicles should be numbered so that they can be matched to the bays. Children can also make numberplates for the vehicles and role play props such as bus-stops, tickets, timetables and speed-limits.

Large scale track games are an effective way of helping children to link physical movement to counting and using number names in order. These can be painted or chalked onto the ground. Tracks might take the form of caterpillars, snakes or snails, may be based around traditional games such as hopscotch, or could be large scale versions of table top track games. Giant dice or spinners can be used for these.

Number rhymes such as 'Five little ducks' and 'Five speckled frogs' can be performed on a much larger and noisier scale out-of-doors, using masks and real logs to bring them to life. Empty green lemonade bottles, labelled from one to ten and set up on a wall, can be used to support the song 'Ten green bottles'. These also offer opportunities for children to order numbers backwards and forwards or find a missing number when setting them up.

These can also be used as a target game, with children throwing beanbags and counting how many are knocked down and how many are left.

There are numerous games that can be played outside to support children's early calculating skills as they keep track of their score. Games involving throwing balls, beanbags or quoits into buckets, through hanging hoops or into chalked shapes are simple but exciting ways of introducing the language of addition. They also provide a meaningful purpose for early recording. Children can keep score in a variety of ways, according to their level of development. These can include:

● using natural objects such as stones or fir cones placed in a pot
● a large scale bead tally, made with ten air flow balls threaded on string and attached to a fence

● drawing simple symbol tallies to represent the objects – for example four circles to denote four balls in the bucket
● using conventional tally marks or numerals chalked on the ground or written on clipboards or easels

● laminated numeral cards, attached together with treasury tags to make a score pad.

When children are collecting natural objects outside, adults should capitalise on the mathematical opportunities. Collections of stones, twigs or leaves can be sorted according to size, shape and colour and patterns and shapes can be explored. Natural objects will add an extra dimension to children's role-play outside. Children can collect the objects they need for their 'recipes' in old saucepans and baskets and prepare them using cooking utensils. This idea can be extended so that children can use pictorial recipe cards when collecting their 'ingredients'.

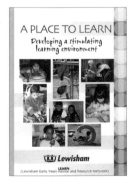

Giant's stew – 3 buttercups, 5 conkers, 2 stones, 3 twigs . . .

Overall, it is important that practitioners do plan to exploit the motivational potential of the outdoor environment and support children's spontaneous learning across all aspects of mathematics.

Kym Scott and Judith Stevens are early years advisers for the London borough of Lewisham.

A place to learn – developing a stimulating learning environment includes a section on developing mathematics out-of-doors as well as promoting mathematics throughout the learning environment. It is published by Lewisham Early Years Service at a cost of £15. Telephone 020 8695 9806

Reference

1 QCA, DfES: ***Curriculum guidance for the foundation stage***, QCA publications, 2000

Solution to Deryns Brand's puzzle on the noticeboard:

$$210 = 2 \times 3 \times 5 \times 7$$
$$770 = 2 \times 5 \times 7 \times 11$$
$$2002 = 2 \times 7 \times 11 \times 13$$
$$4862 = 2 \times 11 \times 13 \times 17$$
$$8398 = 2 \times 13 \times 17 \times 19$$
$$14858 = 2 \times 17 \times 19 \times 23$$

2002

Role play

MATHEMATICAL ADVENTURES IN ROLE PLAY Constance Tyce

The provision of role play is vital in every early years setting. It provides opportunities for the development of all areas of learning. With careful thought and planning, all role play situations can provide children with mathematical adventures.

Many examples of good quality role play had been observed in a variety of settings throughout Norfolk. The early years childcare partnership (EYCP) and the education advisory service decided to work together to organise a series of workshops to promote role play in the foundation stage and celebrate good practice.

Why is role play important?

'*In play a child behaves beyond his average age, above his daily behaviour; in play it is as though he were a head taller than himself.*' (Vygotsky, 1978)

It fosters all aspects of development because it offers children the chance to:

- develop their understanding of the world in their own way and make links between home / community experience and the setting
- represent and act out their ideas and feelings in a safe environment
- live through someone else's experience and develop empathy
- communicate with others in a range of ways including spoken language
- gain access to a broad curriculum in enjoyable, practical and meaningful ways
- develop physical and creative skills and gain a sense of achievement
- develop social skills through collaborating with others

How did we plan to promote role play?

A group of early years advisers invited a group of teachers, pre-school providers, traveller education and social services to plan a series of workshops. These were intended for children and their parents and carers, pre-school providers, teachers and representatives of other agencies working with young children.

The aims of the workshops were:

- to share ideas and enjoyment through successful role play scenarios both indoors and outdoors
- to promote children's learning and creativity through role play, based on real and imaginary experiences
- to enable all parents and adults who work with young children the opportunity to view a variety of role play scenarios

Thirty practitioners, from a range of settings, were involved in planning and presenting the role play scenarios, which included:

- a garden centre
- travel agents
- health centre
- the three bears' cottage
- the jungle
- under the sea
- a trip to the moon

They also had a chance to experience being a lighthouse keeper, getting married, taking a driving test and exploring a traveller's trailer. Rest and refreshments were available in the beach café and the Chinese takeaway. It was important to ensure

The photographs used in this article are by Hilary Scargill, nursery teacher, Sheringham Primary School and Peter Bates, early years advisory teacher, Norfolk.

we included a variety of different role play scenarios, which would develop the children's real and imaginary experiences as well as developing role play outdoors, for example, the driving school and garage.

Each practitioner provided plans to illustrate how they developed the role play scenarios with their children. **Here are two examples:**

How 'exploring pattern in the jungle' links to all six areas of learning

Drayton Community First School. Music corner and animal den.

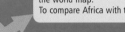

Physical development
To make animal movements.
To create jungle habitat.
To cut, stick, paint, fix and make.
To use a variety of tools to create different effects, (rollers, thick/thin brushes, printing with natural objects.)
To use African instruments.
To dig in sand and mud.

Knowledge and understanding of the world
To investigate animals with spots, stripes and patchwork patterns.
To investigate life in the jungle using reference books, IT and video.
To understand the term grassland and jungle.
To locate Africa on the globe and the world map.
To compare Africa with the UK.

Mathematics
Sorting animals (shape, size, colour and pattern).
Ordering animals to size (big, bigger, biggest) etc.
To count and make sets of animals up to twenty.
To add by combining two sets of animals together.
To develop mathematical language through sand and water play.

Exploring pattern in the jungle

Personal and social development
To share equipment and resources within the jungle.
To take turns and co-operate in jungle games.
To tidy jungle and jungle toys at the end of play.
To develop an understanding and respect for the African culture.
To discuss hunting, exploring and going on safari.
To make their own judgements and opinions.

Language and literacy
To develop descriptive vocabulary to describe patterned animals in the jungle.
To write simple sentences about jungle animals.
To write a daily diary about jungle life.
To listen to a variety of jungle stories and rhymes.
To act out different scenarios based in the jungle.
To read fiction and non-fiction books to gather information about jungle life.

Creative development
To create a jungle habitat.
To explore and make patterned animals, using different materials and media.
To develop role play through different scenarios within the jungle.
To make African music.

Stripy zebras made by the children helped develop number sequencing, but could be adapted for a number of purposes.

The jungle.

Sorting plastic or cuddly jungle animals – number of legs? Patterns? Size? Colour?.

Top left:
The travel agent.
Top right:
Booking a holiday requires a lot of forms to be filled in.
Centre left:
Under the sea.
Centre right:
At the garden centre pet food could be weighed, then bagged up and sold.
Below:
The beach café.

The driving test. Numbered parking spaces were allocated to the correspondingly numbered vehicle.

Example two: travelling to the moon

The second example illustrates how the trip to the moon was first developed through key questions:

- What do we know about the moon?
- What would we like to know about the moon?
- How can we find out more?
- What have we found out?

The children found out the answers to their questions in a variety of ways, for example, verbal discussion, pictures, books, technology such as, ICT, TV and video. Visitors were invited into school to talk to the children. They were also encouraged to talk to their parents.

The 'space travellers' needed a ticket, space currency and a packed lunch before they left. They also needed a health check at the surgery to ensure they were up to the trip.

The teacher then explained to the children that they were going to use their knowledge to create a role play area in the classroom. More questions were asked:

- How can we use what we have found out?
- Who travels to the moon?
- How do they get ready?
- How do they get there?
- What's it like on the moon?

Travelling to the moon

- people who travel to the moon – astronauts
- getting ready to travel on the moon
- protective clothing and equipment

Health checks

- health centre
- doctors, nurses clothing and equipment
- appointment book
- testing eyesight, hearing and fitness
- finger prints
- taking Xrays
- waiting room
- asking 'patients' questions
- make posters related to healthy eating
- labels, notices and signs
- looking after pets in space

The rocket

- structure of the rocket, eg, design roof and windows
- numbered, sequenced seats
- seating plan – matching numbers on ticket to seats
- space maps
- in-flight video, taped music
- count down

Journeying to the moon

- special clothes
- booking office, tickets
- making labels for duty free shop
- exchanging money into 'space money'
- travelling in the rocket
- finding seat number
- buying food and oxygen cylinders, etc
- activities to complete during long journey!

On the moon

- enclosed space area
- space café
- souvenir shop – weighing and money etc
- aliens
- making music

The children were helped to identify the different areas that they would need to develop. They were encouraged to share ideas, plan, design and make each aspect of the role play area.

All the children were involved in the development and therefore the quality of play enabled children to practice skills and develop their thinking.

The workshops

Children and practitioners from pre-school settings, nurseries, reception classes and childminders were invited to attend the Friday workshops and offered hourly sessions during the day. During the session, the children were able to play in the different areas. Each role play area was supported by adults who were able to extend the children's play, provide a good role model, and explain the rationale to the accompanying adults.

We were inundated with requests from settings to attend the workshops and unfortunately had to disappoint many applicants. It was necessary to limit the number of children attending each session to 70 to ensure the different areas were not over-crowded. A total of 750 children accompanied by 200 adults attended the Friday workshops. It was a tremendous response.

The Saturday workshops were also well attended by parents, carers and other practitioners. It was encouraging to see so many parents, carers, grandparents and other family members. Many of the children who had attended the previous day were eager to share the experience with members of their family. All stayed for a considerable length of time, and many adults took part with their children in the activities. Many children were reluctant to leave. The willingness of the adults at each role play scenario to talk with the parents about the value of play was very much appreciated as was the handout, giving further practical ideas about how they could encourage imaginative play at home.

The evaluation of the project

The role play scenarios created had been tried and tested with real children and therefore enabled participants to replicate the ideas in their own settings. The enthusiasm generated by those who provided the role play was both infectious and inspiring for all involved. We were amazed by the range of people who visited including educational officers, advisers, colleagues from other counties and other agencies, teachers and practitioners from a wide range of early years settings, parents and carers, grand parents and other family members and last but not least children of all ages!

The children were very excited but some were slightly overawed initially and tended to gravitate towards familiar activities. As they became more confident they began to explore and investigate new experiences. Gender differences became very

apparent in some areas; for example, the boys tended to monopolise the train set which was available in the small world play area. However it was good to see both boys and girls happy to experience all the other areas. The children displayed a high level of sustained involvement in activities, indicating the extent of their learning. The quality of the children's previous experience of role play was apparent through their response in the different areas. For example some children were able to sustain a high level of involvement in the jungle; cutting up and tasting fruit, sorting the animals, creating their own musical patterns and talking about the sizes and weights of the animals.

Comments received on the evaluation forms completed by practitioners who attended with their children were very positive:

"We had a fantastic time"

"The children wanted to come again the next day"

"Wonderful helpers who supported the children in their play"

"Good accompanying pack"

"Super afternoon – all children and adults thoroughly enjoyed it"

"I think this was a really great experience for the playgroup"

"Very well set up with helpful friendly staff – well worth the journey"

"We loved it"

"BRILLIANT – EXCELLENT – FANTASTIC"

The children found it a valuable experience because:

"I learnt to drive it was great!" – Ngaio

"I went to the jungle and sorted out the animals" – Paul

"It was brilliant in the rocket. I counted lots of stars" – Amanda

"I learnt how to play music in the jungle" – Harry

"I learnt to climb up the lighthouse – it was very high" – Jordan'

The whole project confirmed our belief that good role play can develop children's experiences in all six areas of learning. It was a privilege to work with so many committed and dedicated practitioners who gave so generously of their time and expertise. But most of all it was the response from the children, the joy on their faces as they entered the wonderful world of make believe that made it all worth while. I hope that you will also be inspired to provide similar opportunities for your children.

Constance Tyce is a numeracy adviser with Norfolk LEA.

The quality of the children's previous experience of role play was apparent through their response in the different areas.

Opposite:
Sorting the bears.

References

L.S. Vygotsky, *Mind in society: the development of higher psychological processes*, Harvard University Press, 1978

For ideas of role play areas see Neil Griffiths, *A corner to learn*, Stanley Thornes, 1998

Lesley Hendy, *Imaginative play*, Early Years Educator, Volume 3, No. 3, July 2001

MONEY AND SHOPS, ROLE PLAY AND REAL LIFE

Rose Griffiths

Collecting and making things to set up a post office in class makes children more observant when they go to visit their local post office. Here there were four working areas: The service counter – with till and money, date stamps, etc, postage stamps and leaflets. A customer area – with phones and phone book, and space to sit down and write a letter. The weighing area – with scales and a pile of different size parcels. And an area for shopping for stationery.

Money is probably the most frequently used context for number work in everyday life, for both children and adults, and role play can provide an enjoyable medium for linking children's knowledge of maths in the 'real world' (not just about money) with what they do in an educational setting.

In this article I am going to concentrate on ideas for teachers working with children under 8, but many of the principles apply equally well for older pupils. Role play does not necessarily mean you need to set up special areas in your room – older children can work at their usual desks or tables, taking turns at being the customers or staff of a post office, toy shop, travel agent, car show room or cafe.

How can you make good use of role play shops?

Keep up-to-date

I loved playing at shops when I was a child. My favourite was setting up a post office, because my nan let me run paper through her sewing machine to make perforated sheets of 'stamps'. Real shopping was something I did quite frequently, too; as a child aged 6 or 7, I'd be sent to buy bread or tea from shops several streets away. Quite safe in London in the 1950s.

Things started to change in 1960. I remember all the children in our flats getting very excited when we heard there was a new shop open on the High Street, where you didn't have to ask the shop-keeper for what you wanted and give them your money. Instead, you just helped yourself! We rushed to the new shop and collected big basketsful of tins and packets; we were very disappointed to find that you were expected to pay for everything at the exit. We all agreed this would *never* catch on. After all, how would customers know if they had enough money, without someone adding up for them as they went along?

Supermarkets are now the norm; even the smallest corner shop is now self-service. So a tradi-tional kind of shop is no longer the best model simply because it does not match with most children's experience. Role play about shops and shopping provides children with the opportunity to think about 'real life' where maths helps people solve real problems – but for this to be effective, the setting and props need to be up-to-date.

Change your emphasis depending on the children's age and experience

If you are working with children under 6, you will probably concentrate on issues of sorting and categorising, counting, comparing size directly, and exchanging imaginary money for goods without undue emphasis on how much things cost. Children aged 7 and over are more likely to have sufficient personal experience of shopping and money to benefit from using prices, coins and notes, calculators and mental arithmetic, to buy and sell single items or collections of things.

Have both a shop and a house

Space is at a premium in most classrooms, but children need somewhere to take their shopping, to sort it out and put it away. If you have a shop and a house, you can involve a larger number of children at a time, so you will need less space elsewhere in the class.

Involve children in setting up role play areas

Children can help with making large pieces of role play equipment (for example, painting boxes to make a pretend cooker or sink unit) or collecting or making smaller props. Role play shops sometimes feature a wide variety of single items, but it is more realistic and more useful to have a smaller range of goods, with at least four or five of each item.

Children in Y2 and Y3 helped me make a supermarket full of their own packets of food. We started by looking carefully at some examples of real packets, then used word processing, drawing and photocopying to make packets of 'soup' and labels for small plastic bags of pasta twists, spaghetti, rolled oats and rice. Each packet was filled using scales, so that it weighed exactly what it said on the packet (either 50g or 100g), and children began to be quite good at estimating whether something was about 100g, or a lot more or less.

Items in a play shop are often most useful if they are on a small scale. Large items take up too much space and do not fit into baskets or shopping bags. Intuitive work on scale can be very succesful in a practical context: for example, 'How big should we make pretend pizzas for the shop, compared to the size of plates in the house?'

Discuss the roles of shopkeepers and customers

Talking to children about what they will do when it is their turn for role play helps you to find out what children know about shopping, and helps make their play more purposeful. Explain that three or four children will run the shop whilst three or four play in the house. The shopkeepers could put things on shelves, clean up, write prices and check the till while the shop is closed, and the children in the house could cook, tidy, eat, chat, look after the

babies, count their money and write shopping lists. When the shop is open, the shopkeepers can take turns to be on the checkout, help customers find things, or do their packing. The customers will take their things home and put them away. After a while (usually decided by the teacher) the two groups change roles: the shopkeepers 'finish their shift' and go home, and the former customers go to work in the shop.

Ask children questions whilst they are playing

Encourage them to share experiences and to clarify misconceptions. I found these questions useful:
- How do customers know what things cost?
- How does the shopkeeper know what prices to put on things?
- How do shops arrange things? What do they put together?
- How do you know what you have to pay altogether?
- What money will you give the shopkeeper?
- Where do you get money from? What does a credit card do?
- Why do you take a bag, but you don't put things in it while you're shopping?

A garden gazebo put up in our hall provided the setting for a cafe. Three inexpensive circular chipboard tables had tablecloths made from a jumble-sale duvet cover. There was enough fabric to make some matching aprons, although some children thought they were bibs. A cafe needs a kitchen and somewhere to serve food, menus, notebooks and pencils to take people's orders, and a till. When using the cafe in school, interest was kept high by linking it with real cooking (spaghetti one day, and pancakes on another).

This chip shop was made from an old corner TV cabinet, sprayed silver, with an aluminium camping kitchen rack alongside it. The deep fat fryers are plastic plant pots, also sprayed silver. The chips are plastic ones bought from a local educational supplier, but the fish, pies and mushy peas were made from salt dough. Children measured out big and small portions, counted pies (and chips), used money, talked about time ("The chips will be another five minutes") and shape ("Do you want your chips in a cone?"), and experimented with different ways of wrapping food in rectangles of white paper. Use sturdy cardboard boxes to make a version for your classroom.

The adult's questioning will complement issues raised in the process of playing by children themselves. For example, children discussed the best way of adding up bills, or how to weigh potatoes. Two children had an argument when pricing things in the shop because one of them insisted that bigger things always cost more than smaller ones. The issue was settled the following day, after they had both talked to family and friends and thought of examples (for example, a wrist watch and a tin of beans) to show otherwise.

The previous example illustrates the considerable scope for involving parents and other adults to link role play in school with real life experience. Role play provides opportunities for a mixture of peer-tutoring, work with parents, teacher-intervention and pupils reflecting upon their own experiences. This is a very powerful combination for mathematical learning.

Confront the issue of economic value

Money is a major focus of work in a role play shop, and as a system of measurement of economic value, money has much in common with other measurement systems. However, there are important differences, too. For example, if two people each estimate the height and weight of a teddy bear, they can then use a tape measure and scales to confirm the bear's measurements. It is not as easy to agree upon what it is worth. In real life, the prices of things are determined in many different ways, and prices may change when circumstances change.

When we teach about any other system of measurement, one of our aims is to develop within children a 'feel' for each system so that they can judge whether an answer is reasonable, based on their previous experience and hence their ability to estimate. A desire to 'make the arithmetic manageable' sometimes leads to teachers restricting prices to small amounts in pennies, cutting across children's growing experience of what things cost. A better alternative is to allow children to choose their own prices for goods in their shop. This gives them the opportunity to work at a level they are comfortable with; they are often more ambitious and more successful than their teacher expects.

If a child needs prices kept to small numbers, it may be best to provide a context where that makes sense (for example, a rummage sale's toy stall) or, alternatively, to work with whole pounds. Pounds are only more difficult to cope with when there are pence to deal with at the same time.

Discuss children's work with them

Children I watched writing out price tickets often asked others for their opinion on how much things should be; they also discussed issues such as whether all prices should be the same, to make adding up easier; whether you should only have prices in multiples of ten; why shopkeepers wrote £2.99 when they meant £3; and who had got nice clear writing so you could read their prices. They wrote shopping lists, adverts, bank notes, cheques, credit cards, notices about the shop's opening times, receipts, and a short letter of complaint: 'The shop shud have choclaet'. After talking to the owner of a corner shop on their way back from swimming, one group produced 'stock sheets'. One child wrote a leaflet about 'special offers' and delivered it to children who were still in the home corner, hoping to get them to come shopping straight away! Many children made packets and boxes (sometimes at home) and wrote on information about weight, price, sell-by dates and contents.

Provide sufficient time for children to develop their ideas

Allow a period of weeks for children to develop their ideas both in the role play shop and away from it.

For example, I watched one child being the shopkeeper on three occasions. She played in the shop once or twice a week, over a period of six weeks. She had initially taken random amounts of money when she was 'on the till', and concentrated on packing shopping into bags. She watched other children (and occasionally her teacher) looking at prices, and in the third week she started to take the correct amounts; however she did no adding up, but took the money for each item in a customer's basket separately, including giving change for one item at a time when necessary. After complaints from the queue, she reverted to random amounts for a while, but by the sixth week had developed a method of taking money for two items at a time, using a calculator. Her teacher followed up with practice for her and a friend away from the shop, adding up the prices of two items in their heads, or three or four items on a calculator, and seeing that this gave the same result as counting out the coins for each item separately.

Further thoughts

Once children appreciate the nature of their 'work' when they are role-playing, they can provide ideas and questions themselves to extend their play. Skills and concepts can be developed in contexts which link issues of citizenship and problem-solving.

So . . . what kind of shop are you going to start working on?

Rose Griffiths works for the School Development Support Agency, seconded from the University of Leicester

---

Role play provides opportunities for a mixture of peer-tutoring, work with parents, teacher-intervention and pupils reflecting upon their own experiences. This is a very powerful combination for mathematical learning.

'The shop shud have choclaet'

More than the real thing? . . . one hundred plastic 1p (and 2p) coins cost around £2 from leading educational suppliers

CAN I STILL PLAY WHEN I AM SEVEN? Anne Desforges

Teachers working in the foundation stage have government and research approval to plan for learning through play, which will not only enhance but also promote cognitive development. It is much more difficult for Y2 teachers to justify to colleagues and parents the value of learning through play because despite some powerful research, learning through play still tends to be regarded as a method which allows for recreational rather than rigorous learning. It is our belief that learning through role play can be relevant not only for Y2 pupils but also for Y3 to Y6, where some children are grappling with difficult concepts in maths and would benefit from having these related to real life in a role play scenario.

In this article, it is intended to show that well planned play can give rigour to the maths curriculum in Y2.

Setting up role play

Space is always a problem when providing for role play and I cannot deny that it is much better if you can set out role-play in a large area. Y2 children, however, can work comfortably with role-play provision on tables in a smaller area of the classroom.

Children in the 21st century need a level of sophistication in all areas of education comparable to the experiences in their real lives. This is equally relevant to provision for play. Younger children in reception and Y1 need to have more than one play scenario; for example, a house as well as a shop, hospital or post office, so that the home corner is the reference point and the place where children sort out the shopping, phone for the ambulance or write the letters for posting.

Y2 children do not need the full range of dressing up regalia for them to take on a role. It is good problem-solving for them to have to decide what to wear in order to look like the character they

want to portray – a very wealthy customer, an old lady/gentleman or a cool teenager. It is a useful to have a small set of trays or a shelf where 'customers' can collect purses and money, spectacles, bangles, badges, brooches and other jewellery as well as scarves, ties and maybe shoes and hats. Children who are taking on the role of the workforce in the role-play only need to have badges denoting their roles and these can be designed and made by the children themselves.

Links with other classes in the school can help overcome some of the issues of space as well as providing powerful learning opportunities. Reception classes can use resources created by Y2 children, for example, stamps for the reception post office can be designed and priced in Y2. In addition, Y2 children can be responsible for checking the number of stamps sold, and introducing the weighing and costing of stamps for parcels. Although the curriculum timetable is full, time can be found for these links if they are regarded as worthwhile. Y2 pupils often have to explain their mathematical thinking to an inquisitive four-year-old more rigorously than a teacher can provide within the normal numeracy timetable. Some four-year-olds have also found watching their Y2 classmates at work adding money or measuring, to be inspirational and highly motivating in a way that does not happen when watching another adult modelling the same thing.

Our experience

Within our school we introduce children to a role-play scenario in a series of ways. These may include a visit to the role-play scene in real life, a video taken of a member of staff in the real life scenario, for example; video of a visit by a member of staff to the bank to withdraw or put in money. The video includes interviews with various people in the bank, the post office, the take-away or the car-wash.

Staff carefully research the making of the video beforehand and, of course, it relies on sympathetic

> Y2 pupils often have to explain their mathematical thinking to an inquisitive four-year-old more rigorously than a teacher can provide within the normal numeracy timetable.

staff in the work places visited who will patiently co-operate with the staff's requests. We have found very willing helpers in our visits so far.

A further way of providing the first stimulus for the role-play scenario is to make a book of photographs with a particular focus, for example; showing all the experiences in a garage. These books provide good reference points, as well as being very popular reading resources throughout the life of the scenario.

It is a good idea to use all of these stimuli at some point during the year. Visits to the work place are crucial in order for children to access real life mathematical experiences. Children who have a lot of experience of laundrettes do not necessarily need to visit the launderette again, but a video of the manager's role, involving money and measures is very useful, adding a new dimension to their knowledge of being a customer.

Role play in Y2

Here I have chosen to discuss the DIY centre as a numeracy focus for our Y2 children. This relies on the close co-operation of our local B&Q store. The choice of this scenario, as with all our role play experiences has been heavily influenced by the children. By the age of seven, many children are intrigued by parents' DIY, and eagerly volunteer to help when parents are erecting a new wardrobe, garden table or doing some wallpapering. This

Top left: The final design chosen by reception children from the wallpaper design book.

Top right: At the check out – Y2 pupil working out the cost at £5.00 per roll.

Right: Y2 children in the art area of the classroom packaging the wallpaper rolls ready for collection by reception children.

scenario links with a former experience we provide for children in the foundation stage – of 'wallpapering' the home corner.

The real B&Q is full of interesting mathematical experiences for Y2. To name a few:
- woods of different lengths

- wallpaper pattern books with different exciting patterns using shape in imaginative ways
- tins of paint containing measures such as litres that are often only referred to theoretically in numeracy lessons
- the opportunity to experience values such as £24.99 in a real context
- the opportunity to experience language such as 'dozen' in a context other than eggs.

The DIY centre gives Y2 children opportunities to learn about measures, shape and money as well as the opportunity to think about where maths helps people to solve problems. But they cannot do this without the tools for the job and props need to be appropriate – for example providing a variety of measuring tapes as opposed to school rulers and metre sticks.

Involving the children

After the initial visit, the children brainstorm their ideas, listing what they will need.

lengths of dowel, saws, sandpaper, a woodwork bench, goggles, rolls of plain paper for making wallpaper, a pricing gun, a cash till, the manager's accounting book.

One child even suggested an area for a staff room!

In order to make the experience more realistic we arranged for children to purchase some tins of paint so that they could relate the measure to a real cost in their role-play. The colours were chosen carefully and sold on to staff afterwards!

Three areas were chosen – a wood area, a wallpaper and paint area and the cash point/ ordering area.

The children used two shelving units already in the classroom to make the sales area and took weeks cutting doweling into varying lengths of centimetres and labelling them for sale at so much per centimetre. Children became quite good at estimating how many centimetres long a piece of doweling was. They made a table showing a quick price guide for the customer.

They also studied the old wallpaper books and then made their own designs transposing them from paper onto the computer. Their designs began with shapes and repeating patterns, but developed into other designs such as making borders to match.

They decided on the length for a wallpaper roll and used some of the art curriculum time to print out their designs before pricing them at £5.00 per

roll. Because of space, it was decided that no roll would measure more than a metre. After printing off their designs they put them into a book containing more than a hundred pages and numbered the pages.

Some children worked at designing order forms for wallpaper asking for the number of rolls required, choice of colour and giving both an order date and a delivery date six weeks later, involving work with calendars.

After discarding the usual cash registers for play, because they did not have the appropriate space and compartments, children made themselves a till from a cardboard box, which they divided into sections for coins, notes and cheques. This was a progression from their previous use of toy cash registers in reception and Y1. Children also visited the school office to observe cheques being written before designing some of their own.

Most of this work was done as part of the time tabled numeracy lessons, but we also used art & technology time. In our view, approaching a numeracy lesson in this way brings a change of routine for both us and the children.

At half term Y2 were ready to open the centre, and made posters advertising the forthcoming date to be displayed around the school.

Deciding on the different roles

Talking to the children about the different roles in the centre revealed how much they knew about the roles of the manager and the sales assistant, together with the skills needed to do a good job at the checkout and in the ordering department.

Children in Y2 were very keen to get opening times correct and even wanted to have wage packets and slips for the staff as well as some form of clocking on and off machine. This was an extension of the original plan and children used the school's forms for supply teachers to look at how to keep a record of when staff had worked and how many hours work had been carried out. It was soon obvious that there was more than a term's work in this scenario if time permitted.

Children developed rota forms for the sales assistants, the manager and the checkout assistant. At first the rota was fairly crude with only names of 'staff' but it was soon developed into a more sophisticated format with times when staff clocked on and off. This involved using digital clocks to aid recording.

The children designed a wage slip and talked about how much money a sales assistant should earn for each hour. They then filled in the timesheets for a week and calculated how much money was earned.

When the centre was open, children worked at replenishing the shelves, identifying which length of wood was selling the fastest and which design of wallpaper was the most popular. Later, it was decided to sell off those designs that were not popular at a reduction of 50p per roll. This took time to work out and some children had to get out the cost of a roll in terms of cash and physically take away the 50p, totalling the remainder, whilst other children used their heads.

We made sure that children used real money and this naturally had to be counted out each morning and back in at the end of the day by the cashier.

Further developments

The news of the project soon spread throughout the school and after seeing the Y2 design book, reception children asked if they could come to Y2 to order some wallpaper for their home corner. This was arranged and reception children 'travelled in their cars' along the corridor to the DIY centre, orders were placed and a date arranged for collection. This real context added a new dimension to the Y2 work and children went to the reception area to measure the walls and to work out how much wallpaper would be needed, thus adding customer services to their repertoire.

Reception children used a calendar to count off the days until the order was ready. When the wallpaper was ready, the children in Y2 packaged up the rolls in one of the bags they had made and designed. The child on the checkout that day had to use his fingers to help add up the total amount of six rolls at £5.00 each.

This experience with another year group was so successful, that Y2 went on to make a book of curtain designs and to measure up the window in the reception home corner for curtains to match the wallpaper.

Assessment issues

We encouraged children to form their own questions whilst playing and to write those questions in the form of a word bubble. These were then mounted around the play area and became the focus for discussion between staff and children.

Some of the questions from the DIY project included:

- Where does the shopkeeper get more wood when it has all been sold?
- Have you seen anyone measure material – how

did they do it?
- How are things priced on the shelves in B&Q?
- Is there an easy way to find out the total when something costs £5.00 each?
- Is it better to pay with money or a cheque?
- How do you check how much you have spent before you get to the check out?

There was a lot of scope for the teacher to assess different children's learning styles in mathematics.

It was interesting to observe the children who had been through the school and had experienced role-play in reception and Y1 and compare them with those children who had come into the school during the previous year with little or no experience of learning through play. The children with experience of role-play showed more problem-solving strategies than those who had little or no experience of maths through role-play. For example, they were able to add sums of money together without resorting to coins for help and they were able to write down sums of money in pounds and pence. A few children who struggled with numbers above ten in the more formal classroom situation were more confident using larger numbers in the DIY centre when learning was related to real life experiences.

Some children found it difficult to work out anything without resorting to pencil and paper despite the focus on mental maths in the numeracy strategy. Some children showed surprising talent with measurement and shape when art and maths were used together, in designing their wallpaper patterns.

And finally . . .

The DIY centre lasted for the whole term, allowing children time to work on problem-solving in depth. Big books were made for each DIY area, showing the maths learned through the children's own eyes and these were used for children's reference and to inform the planning for the same project the following year.

Whether in a small area of the classroom on tabletops or in a larger area, this project offers children the opportunity to learn about measures and money in a relevant and stimulating context.

The experience provided information for the teacher to follow up in more structured numeracy sessions. Planned play for Y2 is certainly not recreational. When given the opportunity, the appropriate resources and challenge, children make sure that it lives up to the rigours of real life!

Anne Desforges teaches at Deepdale Infants School, Preston.

We made sure that children used real money and this naturally had to be counted out each morning and back in at the end of the day by the cashier.

We encouraged children to form their own questions whilst playing and to write those questions in the form of a word bubble. These were then mounted around the play area and became the focus for discussion between staff and children.

Discussions on children's learning

THE BABY WITH THE BATH WATER Ruth Merttens

> Recently, with the dissemination of the *Curriculum guidance for the foundation stage* [1], we have witnessed a return to some of the unhelpful dichotomies and polarised positions that have plagued early years education since the seventies.

Currently we are in the middle of a bit of an ideological crisis in the early years. Two years ago we had the national numeracy strategy, which presaged a sea change in maths education, and in particular in some of the practices we use in reception and Y1 classes. On the whole, these changes were well received by both teachers and parents – and most importantly, they were popular with children. For the first time in more than twenty years, we saw a return to children sitting on the rug, cheerfully counting in unison to one hundred and beyond. However, recently, with the dissemination of the *Curriculum guidance for the foundation stage* [1], we have witnessed a return to some of the unhelpful dichotomies and polarised positions that have plagued early years education since the seventies.

Play or work, formal or informal, abstract or concrete – these are the 'goody-baddy' dualisms against which all debate about early years is now structured. Bad is formal teaching, as opposed to informal learning. Good is free play as opposed to working in rows. Bad is abstract maths as opposed to concrete practical activities. And so-on and so-forth. But anyone, parent or teacher, who works in the early years, knows that life refuses to be thus constrained within such neat categories. God made the spectrum, but man makes the pigeonholes. And, as Freud famously remarked, the devil is always in the detail. In the detailed welter of classroom life, none of these hard distinctions hold water. Is it formal teaching if I teach my class a nursery rhyme, chanting together, 'One, two, three, four, five. Once I caught a fish alive . . .'? Are the children playing or working if they are playing snakes and ladders or hopping along a hopscotch line in the playground? Is jumping a frog along a number track abstract mathematics or concrete activity? Can any playgroup or nursery honestly argue that teaching is bad and learning is good when the former can precipitate so much of the latter?

> Teaching and learning may best be seen as two sides of the same piece of paper.

Vygotsky [2] argued with Piaget that, whilst learning can be seen, partially at least, as a function of development, the role of teaching is crucial:

> '[Piaget] considers instruction and development to be mutually independent. Development is seen as a process of maturation subject to natural laws, and instruction as the utilisation of opportunities created by development . . . Thus instruction creates the potentialities, and development realises them. Education is seen as a kind of superstructure erected over maturation . . .
>
> On the contrary, according to us, in the child's development imitation and instruction play a major role. They bring out the specifically human qualities of the mind and lead the child to new developmental levels. In . . . learning school subjects, imitation is indispensable. What the child can do in co-operation today, he can do alone tomorrow. Therefore the only good kind of instruction is that which marches ahead of development and leads it . . .'

Teaching and learning may best be seen as two sides of the same piece of paper. We can choose to focus exclusively on one side only, but cut one and you cut the other. Direct teaching can often produce learning, and learning just as frequently leads on to some further teaching. At home, as much as in school, the parent demonstrates and the child copies. Teaching my small son to sew, I was using exactly such a pedagogy. Imitation, as Vygotsky said, is indispensable to learning. Teaching and learning can be construed as demonstration and imitation as faithfully as they can be construed as facilitating and discovering. It depends upon what is being learned, by how many and in what context.

Just as children *learn* in a number of situations – and the foundation stage guidance makes it clear that a variety of different play and learning settings should be provided by nurseries and playgroups – so we can *teach* in a variety of different contexts.

Some things are best taught to a large group, and demonstration and modelling (by the teacher), imitation and repetition (by the children), all play a major part. Other things are best approached in the context of the small group, and facilitating a discussion between children or extending a play activity best describe the most appropriate teaching here. Helping children to lay a table, matching cutlery to people, or to butter and fold a sandwich, are certainly most usefully taught as the need arises and in the course of the children's own activities. By contrast, counting to ten, or matching a number to a quantity, may both be modelled most effectively to all the children during circle time.

Many – even most – children enjoy what might be described as the ritual aspects of maths. Learning to count is a comforting and pleasurable ritual. From the pushchair upwards many children chant the numbers in order with their parents as they put on their coats or jump along the paving stones. As soon as children arrive in the nursery or playgroup we can build on these home practices by counting all together and matching the numbers to our fingers. Working in schools on the continent many years ago, I was impressed by the plethora of different activities in which young children were encouraged to listen to spoken numbers and respond in just this way using their fingers. These teacher-initiated activities mainly occurred in a large group situation. The children put their hands behind their backs. "Show me six!" encourages the teacher, "ready, steady, go!" And the children bring out their hands with six fingers standing up and four folded down. The teacher draws attention to the fact that some children have shown six as three fingers on each hand, whereas others have shown five on one hand and one on the other. In a similar situation, the cloth bag also makes a good model. The teacher holds the bag and chooses a child to place four small teddies into it while the rest count them in. "How many teddies now?" she asks, placing another teddy in the bag. The children are tripping over themselves to tell her there are five!

Activities like these have re-surfaced in English schools as part of the ways of working encouraged by the *Framework for teaching mathematics* [3]. At the same time, teachers have been supported in talking a more analytic approach to the teaching of operations – for example, introducing addition through counting on one or two more, rather than as the combination of two sets. For years in England and Wales, we have watched children counting three things in one set, counting four things in a second, and then putting the sets together and counting the lot. On the continent, I worked with teachers who took it for granted that we would start with a

number of objects, match these to the number, spoken or written, and then increase the set by one or two. From the start, the children are thus encouraged to count *on*. It is, of course, the image of the number line which underpins these ways of working and the colourful pegged number line, hanging well within the children's reach, is hopefully becoming a standard item in every nursery or playgroup.

As we discuss the detail of the activities we might productively use in teaching young children maths, we become ever more aware that the 'goody-baddy' distinctions that we referred to at the start of this article fail to hold water in the messy realities of the classroom. Are the number rhymes and the counting together formal maths? Yes, if by this we mean that they are teacher-initiated. No, if by this we mean that it is necessary to be sitting in quiet rows doing dull work which makes no sense. Children are justly proud if they have learned a rhyme or can successfully count to ten. They are pleased to extend these skills and quickly become confident at doing so in the 'safe' environment of the large group. Is moving a counter – sometimes a human one! – along a number track abstract rather than concrete mathematics? Yes, if we take concrete in the Piagetian sense of the word meaning to match numbers to quantities of objects, and no if we use the term to indicate a context or event which makes sense to children. It is crucially this 'making sense' which I believe should under-write all our activities with children and which enables both good modelling and discovery learning.

All of us in education who are parents know if we are honest, that we have, on occasion, 'formally' taught our own children. We know from the evidence of our own experience, as well as from research, that the young children who engage in ritual home practices such as counting and rhyming, memorising songs and chanting numbers in order, are precisely those children who are likely to start school at the best advantage. Unfortunately, many children come to school without having participated in this type of activity. We do them no favours whatsoever if we fail to provide these learning opportunities once they reach an educational context. For some children, it may make little or no difference, since these are routine practices at home. For others, it may act to reinforce their disadvantage. For the sake of these, the most vulnerable, it is to be hoped that the myths surrounding the new foundation stage curriculum do not encourage teachers to throw out the baby with the bath water.

Ruth Merttens is an early years specialist and co-directs the Hamilton maths and reading projects.

> We know from the evidence of our own experience, as well as from research, that the young children who engage in ritual home practices such as counting and rhyming, memorising songs and chanting numbers in order, are precisely those children who are likely to start school at the best advantage.

References:

1 DfEE/QCA: *Curriculum guidance for the foundation stage*, QCA, 2000

2 L. Vytgotsky, *Mind in society*, Harvard University Press, 1978

3 DfEE/QCA: *National numeracy strategy; framework for teaching mathematics from reception to year 6*, Cambridge University Press, 1999

ATTITUDE IS EVERYTHING

Zoë Rhydderch-Evans

In his book **Wise up**, Guy Claxton [1] engages his reader in deep thought about the skills and the temperament that we require to become an accomplished 'learner'. I just wish he could have written and presented me with this book right at the start of my teaching career. As it happens I believe that I came to share many of Professor Claxton's theories about young children's learning and incorporated them into my practice in the teaching of mathematics through long years of failures and successes. My first reading of his book confirmed, endorsed and greatly extended what I had come to believe.

Rarely, if ever, when focusing on the learning of mathematics at the foundation stage, do we make it our priority to let children get to grips with the kind of subject mathematics is. Rarely do we put our planning energy into devising strategies which will encourage our young pupils to develop the resilience and persistence needed to be comfortable with a subject which presented Einstein with problems!

I want to suggest that a positive and realistic attitude to the subject would be the best gift we could offer to our young and emergent mathematicians, hence my title – *Attitude is everything*. There is a question we must answer so that we can get to grips with the mathematical needs of young children. What is it about mathematics that fascinates those who love it? What motivates lovers of this subject so much that they acquire the resilience and persistence needed to struggle with a mathematical problem for hours on end? Regardless of our mathematical competence, we are all quite capable of

acquiring this insight. It is surprising how much vicarious experience one can gain by reading fascinating biography and autobiography. Books which let you into the secret of what it is that turns mathematicians on are of the ilk of **Fermat's last theorem** by Simon Singh [2] which the **Daily Mail** critic claimed 'read like the chronicle of an obsessive love affair' [1].

For the rest of this article I want to concentrate on the three qualities that Guy Claxton claims constitute a good learning temperament and suggest ways in which we can nurture those qualities in our everyday practice. The qualities are:
- Resilience and persistence
- A playful disposition
- Conviviality

> There is a question we must answer so that we can get to grips with the mathematical needs of young children. What it is about mathematics that fascinates those who love it?

Resilience and persistence

My interpretation of what Guy Claxon's has to say about resilience and persistence is quite straightforward. It does children no good at all if we continually make things too easy for them and thus give them a false picture of what learning is really like. He says that children need to get used to dealing with frustration, confusion and apprehension because they are feelings that all learners will experience and must learn to cope with and see as quite normal and be unfazed by. It should go without saying that the only way one could allow children to experience these feelings would be in a very safe and supportive classroom environment. I like this message enormously because I grew up thinking that if you were good at mathematics you could solve problems at a first attempt. If I couldn't find a solution immediately I thought it was because I wasn't clever enough. If ever there was a subject where one needs to be able to enjoy an intellectual tussle, surely it is mathematics? I therefore see it as critical that we gentle our young children into problem-solving by continually demonstrating a problem-tackling approach where we do not allow solutions to be found too easily.

A playful disposition

Claxton maintains that all learners need a playful disposition in order to be successful whether they are child or adult. He says that play and learning are not different things but that play is a kind of learning which leaves a residue which is a more robust, playful inquisitive kind of mentality. Now here is a cause for celebration. All early years' practitioners know that children need to learn through experience and play and here is an eminent professor encouraging us to give children their experience in a playful way.

Conviviality

Claxton's philosophy maintains that good learners can share ideas and toss them about with others. Good learners speak their thoughts aloud with others, share doubts with others. A major task at the foundation stage is to help children to speak and comprehend the language of mathematics. Our teaching practice will need to provoke children into discussion and into speaking their thoughts aloud in order to share them with others.

Embracing the philosophy

I am convinced that choosing the right 'stuff' [apparatus if you like] to embed and contextualise, the processes we are introducing needs very careful thought. If we are to have any chance of success with our introduction of new learning our 'stuff' has to allow us to put the mathematical experiences we plan for the children into a context which fully engages them. If we fail to choose appropriately it is unlikely that the children will be motivated enough to enter into the sustained effort which problem solving demands. I have strong anti-feelings about some of the coloured plastic which is often heavily relied on as a teaching and learning aid and which often proves to be something less than exciting.

Here are some of my criteria for choosing material:
- It has to be attractive enough to make the children excited about working with it and to sustain their attention
- It has to relate to children's real world or fantasy experiences
- It has to allow the children to hear mathematical language in pragmatic situations that make the meaning of the terms obvious and provoke our pupils into using the words themselves
- It has to enable the demonstration of the

Photographs of Zoë working with the children were taken at St Julian's Infant School, Newport, South Wales.

various processes that we carry out in mathematics

- It has to allow us to embed problem-solving in a context that encourages a playful approach.

If we apply these criteria I believe we have a much better chance of planning experiences which make 'human sense' to the children (Margaret Donaldson's term [3]).

A session with the children – stuff

Most children love animals and are only too happy to discuss their pets. Problem-solving which maps on to this interest will usually appeal to them. About a year ago McDonalds were giving away small toy Dalmatians which ranged in size from a length of approximately 10 centimeters to about 15 centimeters. Most children have got a couple lurking in their toy boxes at home. It should therefore be fairly easy to put out an appeal in a school and put a collection together. You might even get 101!

Next you will want some baskets for the dogs. A raid on the recycling box and a design technology session should provide you with a set in various shapes. Alternatively collect small baskets in a range of shapes. You have all you need for some structured experiences.

Working with this 'stuff' should provide the children with experience of:

- **Volume:** looking at the amount of space within a container
- **Area:** looking at the surface area of the base and seeing how much of it they have covered
- **Counting:** to find how many dogs have been put in each time a basket is filled
- **Comparison of group sizes:** comparing the numbers of dogs put into the different baskets
- **Shape:** comparing the shape of the base of each basket, counting the number of sides by tracing the edges with their fingers.

Of course the children's awareness of these mathematical elements will be increased by appropriate dialogue, such as:

'Let's look at the bottom of this basket. Do you think the bottom is big enough for us to get 3 of our dogs in here? Does anybody think that it is big enough to get more than 3 in here?'

Now let's examine a problem-solving session to demonstrate the approach I've been suggesting. Teacher talk will be in blue.

Context for problem: *Who has a pet? Where do they like to go to sleep? Whose dog has a bed of their own? What does the dog's bed look like? Does anybody have more than one dog? Do they share a bed?*

Conviviality

Sit the children in a circle on the carpet. Leave enough space in the middle to manipulate the 'stuff'. Place the children carefully next to a 'talking partner'. You will know which children work well together. One child might be a very good partner for another who is very shy or less articulate. One child might be confident in the sort of situation they are about to encounter and would be able to support another who is less sure.

The problem

You've been telling me about the kind of beds that your dogs like to sleep in. We've made some beds for our dogs. I think we might do some problem solving now. We'll need to be mathematicians.

Supposing that we had 6 dogs but only 2 baskets. How many different ways do you think that we could put the dogs into the baskets?

Encouraging a playful disposition

The playful disposition, the 'have-a-go' attitude will need modeling for the children.

Can I have the first go? I'm going to pick up some of the dogs and put them in the large basket.

I select 4 Dalmatians from the set.

I'm going to put the rest into the smaller basket. 'The rest' is of course 2.

Engaging in the activity

Once the dogs have been put in the baskets they will need to be counted and comparisons made. A range of questions may be asked, such as:

What can you tell me about he number of dogs in the baskets?

Are there the same number of dogs in each basket or is there a number difference?

Which basket has the most dogs in it? Which has the fewest?

Let's take the dogs out of both baskets and see if we can put them in so that we have the same number of dogs in each basket.

Let's take the dogs out of the small basket and put them into the large basket with the others. How many will be in the large basket now?

Resilience and persistence (and conviviality and playfulness)

The main part of the task is to find as many different ways of partitioning the set of dogs between the two baskets as we can. Now we need to pursue it.

Who think that they can put the dogs into the baskets in a different way?

Have a talk with your friend and see if you can come up with an idea.

Once the children have discovered a different way, for example 5 and 1; it will be essential that a way of recording the different pairings is devised otherwise it will be extremely difficult to remember what has been tried and what has not. Getting the children to devise a pictorial form of recording gives them ownership of their work and allows them to read and interpret it. Early forms of recording have to be more than colouring in exercises if they are to help internalise the processes carried out.

To find different ways of putting the dogs into the baskets will require playfulness and this in turn will generate the fun, which motivates the persistence needed to sustain the investigation. To support the children I often have a toy alongside me, which can whisper suggestions that only I or the child holding it can understand. A favourite of mine is a toy dragon, which makes a soft grumbling sound when you squeeze its tummy.

The ideas that the dragon whispers to me don't always work. When this happens my reaction is to say very positively 'Good idea but it didn't work, you'll have to have another go'. It is essential that we demonstrate to the children that mathematics is not a get-it-right-first-time subject. They must know that persistence and resilience are called for. Over time I want the children to become confident enough to try out ideas without expecting that every one will be successful. The joy is that every time we try something we know something.

By the time three or four ideas have been tried out the children could well be getting tired so the following dialogue might be called for.

How can we be sure that we have found all the ways that are possible? It isn't easy is it? I'm feeling

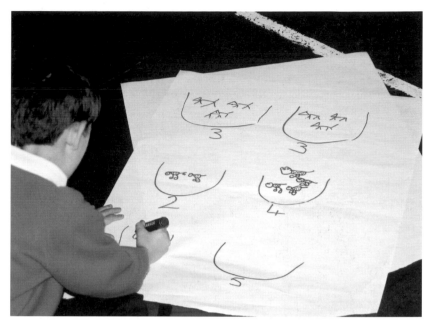

a bit tired now. I've got brain ache. Have you?

I think we could leave it for today but we'll come back to it tomorrow.

Who knows! Tomorrow we might encounter commutativity and get into deep discussion about whether 2 + 4 and 4 + 2 are different pairings or the same.

Attitude is everything: Conviviality, playfulness, resilience, persistence are such important dispositions to nurture in the young mathematician. We dare not neglect them if children are to succeed. I am eternally grateful to Guy Claxton. I was so excited after reading his book to realise that in my work with young children I had been encouraging these very dispositions. My understanding has now increased a hundredfold. I recommend 'Wise up' to all teachers of mathematics whatever the age of their students.

Zoë Rhydderch-Evans worked for many years as teacher and headteacher. She is now an independent early years consultant.

Early forms of recording have to be more than colouring in exercises if they are to help internalise the processes carried out.

Footnote

1 Simon Singh is one of the key speakers at ATM's 2003 Easter Conference. See Noticeboard, p8, for more details.

References

1 Guy Claxton: *Wise up – the challenge of lifelong learning*. Bloomsbury Press, 1999. ISBN 0-7475-4069-1

2 Simon Singh: *Fermat's last theorem*. Fourth Estate, 1997. ISBN 1-85702-669-1

3 Margaret Dondaldson: *Children's minds*. Fontana/Collins, 1978. ISBN 0-006335287-1

THE IMPORTANCE OF TRIALLING Sheila Ebbutt

The early childhood maths group has been working with BEAM to develop a set of early years' number track games. There are five A2 track boards, double-sided. On one side there is the track set in a context, such as with dinosaurs, and on the other the plain track. The games are for children in the foundation stage. Here is an example of a game to be played on a numbered spiral track.

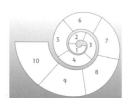

Georgeous things

For 2 to 4 players.
You need:

- at least 55 gorgeous things (buttons, feathers, sequins...)
- a collecting board with ten spaces for each player
- 1 to 10 spinner

Put one gorgeous thing on 1, two gorgeous things on 2, three gorgeous things on 3, and so on, up to 10.

Take turns to:

- spin the spinner and say the number
- take a gorgeous thing from that number on the board
- put it in a space on your collecting board

If the gorgeous things have gone from that number, you can choose where to take one from. Keep going until everybody has collected ten things.

The games were written by experienced practitioners, who know a thing or two about young children. But, as always, we sent the boards and the games out for trialling. And it's a good thing we did too. No matter how much you know, and how much you think about what you've written, children will always surprise you!

Here are some of the things we found out from our triallers.

Children playing

Older children become experts and teach younger children, so make sure you teach the older children too. The games are mostly for two children - but it's helpful to have two children watching while they are waiting to have a go, while another two play. That way, the next pair already knows how to play, and they may have developed some strategies while watching. Sometimes a game for three worked better with two, or a game for two worked better with four playing as two pairs. But sometimes a game worked well for two, then more children came to join, and the game became too slow. Sometimes a crowd of spectators chipped in and advised.

Lesson for writers: Always try out games and find out the optimum number it needs to play them. Make sure the timing is right – not too quick and not too slow.

Lesson for practitioners: Be prepared to adapt the number of children playing to suit the children. Get children to teach children.

What we missed out in the instructions

Something always happens in a game that you don't think of when you write the instructions. Although adults working with young children have to be endlessly flexible and quick witted, it helps to have predicted some tricky moments.

- The instructions say that each child starts with six counters, but doesn't say that the children need to count out the counters first.
- Do you have to throw the exact number to win?
- Where do you start? End?
- What if I've got some counters left over?
  Lesson for writers: Always try out games first.
  Lesson for practitioners: Be prepared to make up arbitrary rules on the spot.

Winners

Many triallers reported that children liked playing co-operatively, rather than for a winner. This worked particularly well when each player had to remember to do complicated things, like put things on one side of the board. They liked to do these things together. Games were more successful without an air of competition. If there were winners, they preferred first winner, second winner . . . Sometimes the winner could be the one with the most, sometimes the one with the least. The children liked these variations. But often, there was

no clear end to the games, nor a winner. The children just enjoyed the process of playing.

Lesson for writers and practitioners: Don't assume children are competitive. Don't assume children cannot co-operate.

Adapting the games

Many of the triallers changed the games on the hoof with the children. They used dice instead of a spinner, put cards out on the table instead of into a bag, used a spinner instead of taking a handful of counters . . . Some things feel like a good idea when you are writing, but the children can find them cumbersome and an exciting game becomes dull. It's a very subtle thing! We received many suggestions for simplifications and extensions to the games. Many triallers left the board and objects out, and the children adapted the games for themselves.

Lesson for writers: Provide a range of simplifications, extensions and variations. Remember, children often don't learn what you intend them to learn.

Lesson for practitioners: As always, be a lateral thinker and have a dozen alternative ideas up your sleeve.

We developed and trialled games for young children. But the same principles apply to whatever you write for any age children, be it games, activities, lessons or worksheets. Get children to try them and be your critics and reviewers. There is a proliferation of teaching material nowadays – publishing is so much easier, and we all have computers. But so much of the material is not well written or thought out, because it has not been tried out with either teachers or children. Games are particularly subtle in the way they work. Just a small change in the numbers playing, in the rules, in the equipment . . . can make a dull game exciting, and vice versa.

Sheila Ebbutt is a director of BEAM, specialist mathematics publishers and course providers.

The games Sheila refers to in this article are **Number track games** available from BEAM 020 7684 3330 / 3323. They cost £19.50 (plus VAT) for five, laminated, full-colour A2 boards, with track in context one side, and numbered track the other. They come with a book containing 60 different games to play at different levels on the tracks.

THE PLACE OF USING AND APPLYING MATHEMATICS

Alison Price with the KS1 & 2 and working group [1]

> One teacher commented that problem-solving activities in number were more difficult to find.

With the introduction of the latest national curriculum [2] using and applying mathematics retained its attainment target within the level descriptions, but the programme of study was integrated into the programmes of study for curriculum content (number, shape, space and measures). This brought it in line with the national numeracy strategy, which does not identify using and applying mathematics as a separate topic.

The KS1&2 working group have been exploring teachers' understanding of the place of AT1, 'using and applying mathematics', now that use of the national numeracy strategy and the new national curriculum has been established in most primary schools.

Discussion was initiated by some members of the group having read Hughes et al [3], in which the authors explore teaching mathematics for application in English and Japanese classrooms. The group felt that within the national numeracy strategy NNS framework [4]:

- there were recognisable 'problem-solving' sections which encourage children to use the mathematics they already know in the context of 'real life' problems
- there was significant evidence of using and applying mathematics in terms of teaching strategies – getting children to explain and reason etc.

However the group were unsure whether teachers were recognising these activities as relating to AT1, or whether they were assessing children's achievement within these activities.

> While the mathematics of these activities was recognised, there was little mention of these being opportunities to assess AT1.

Members collected a range of informal data by talking to teachers in their schools, and in one case devising a simple questionnaire given to all the teachers in a small infant school. The questions asked by everyone related to the knowledge of the curriculum for using and applying mathematics, how using and applying mathematics was carried out in the classroom and how it was assessed.

Results

Teachers at all key stages knew that using and applying mathematics was still present in the new curriculum. Reception teachers cited M11 (*use developing mathematical ideas and methods to solve practical problems*) in the foundation stage early learning goals as related to AT1 [5]. Although they did not mention process skills incorporated in the other goals, for example the children's use of language to communicate mathematical ideas. Examples of problem solving given at the foundation stage included everyday practical activities within the classroom such as sorting out toys, and comparative measures. One teacher commented that problem-solving activities in number were more difficult to find.

Regarding the national curriculum, KS1&2 teachers knew that AT1 was incorporated into programmes of study for number (AT2) and shape, space and measures (AT3). However no-one mentioned the need to assess AT1 separately from AT2 &3. Mention was made most often to the sections on problem solving in the NNS framework. KS1 teachers talked of addition and subtraction of money, solving problems and a range of cross curricular activities including baking, gardening, measuring time in PE, design technology (especially for using and applying measures), and direction in geography. Again, while the mathematics of these activities was recognised, there was little mention of these being opportunities to assess AT1.

However, some teachers also commented on the scarcity of opportunities for 'real' problem solving within the confines of the daily mathematics lesson. They felt that it was difficult to bring the 'real world' into the structured lesson and found that mathematics schemes concentrated more on word problems. One teacher commented that the HBJ scheme was good for real problems [6];

'A lovely scheme to dip into, but not enough structure for everyday.'

One member of the group suggested the introduction of the occasional 'Not the numeracy hour day' (ntnhd) when a more real problem-solving approach could be adopted. The KS1 teachers did not mention the teaching and assessment of mental strategies, or the demands made on the children to explain their thinking as being related to using and applying mathematics and assessed under AT1.

At foundation stage and KS1 therefore, there seemed to be a range of activities within and outside the daily mathematics lesson when using and applying mathematics are taking place, although opportunities for assessment were not necessarily being taken.

KS2 teachers recognised the importance of problem solving and investigational work and seemed more aware of the opportunities for reasoning, explaining and using patterns offered by the mental and oral approach to calculation. Examples were offered of children justifying their answers, and the explicit use of pattern within the 100 square and number system to aid calculation. However, at this key stage a different problem arose. The tendency to use setting within, and sometimes across, year groups, meant that teachers and children were only constituted as a class within the structure of the numeracy lesson. In contrast to KS1, opportunities for more extended pieces of work, for developing using and applying mathematics in other subject areas and the assessment of these were very limited. Lessons tended to be clearly focused, offering little opportunity for children to select and use equipment, and problems of access to ICT in particular were mentioned at KS2 (no-one mentioned ICT at all at KS1).

Overall, teachers' confidence in teaching U&A varied from *'very confident, no problems'* to *'not very confident'* and *'I would need to look at the programmes of study to remind myself'*.

Assessment

Early years' and KS1 teachers talked a lot about assessment through observation of practical activities and questioning, but not often through written work;

'I feel that recording their answers is the least important part – it's more important that they understand what they are doing'.

Teachers gave examples of activities children had done where U&A was obviously relevant such as a child making a model vehicle in design and technology. However few teachers indicated that they were using such activities as an opportunity to assess against AT1 objectives and one Y2 teacher commented;

'I don't think we are concentrating on AT1 learning objectives because they are woolly, but numeracy learning objectives are our daily focus'.

At KS2, despite the increasing use of assessment within this key stage [7], there was little discussion of assessment of AT1.

Some conclusions

All teachers seemed aware of much of the relevant curriculum for using and applying mathematics within the various curriculum documents. Teachers of both key stages focussed on problem solving when responding, as well as commenting on the difficulties of using realistic problems within the structure of the daily mathematics lesson. Foundation and KS1 teachers were also aware of the range of mathematics being used in other subject areas, while KS2 teachers had less opportunity to relate mathematics teaching to other areas of the curriculum. KS2 teachers did seem more aware that opportunities for reasoning and explaining within the numeracy strategy related to using and applying mathematics.

The group concluded that the following issues needed to be explored further:

- Do we recognise teaching strategies used within the numeracy strategy as opportunities to develop and assess children's communication and reasoning as identified in the programmes of study? At KS2 this includes opportunities to select and use appropriate mathematics within highly focused teaching.

- Can we develop and share a wider range of realistic problems as starting points for using and applying mathematics, rather than just de-contextualised word problems?

- Can we use opportunities to assess children against AT1 across the curriculum and not just in 'problem-solving' activities within the daily mathematics lesson?

Alison Price is a senior lecturer in primary mathematics education at Oxford Brookes University.

References

1 The KS1&2 working group consists of teachers who meet once a term on a Saturday in Oxford to explore issues of teaching mathematics in the primary school. Most members teach in reception, KS1 and KS2 classes and special schools. We welcome new members and further details can be obtained from alison-price@atm.org.uk

2 DfEE/QCA, *The national curriculum*, HMSO, 1999

3 M. Hughes, C. Desforges, C. Mitchell, *Numeracy and beyond: applying mathematics in the primary school*, Open University, 2000

4 DfEE, *The national numeracy strategy: framework for teaching mathematics from reception to Y6*, HMSO, 1999

5 DfEE/QCA, *Curriculum guidance for the foundation stage*, HMSO, 2000

6 *HBJ Mathematics*, Harcourt, Brace and Janovich Ltd, 1990

7 Optional SATs (standard assessment tests) were being used in many schools at the end of each year.

SOME ELEMENTS OF PROOF IN KS1 SHAPE AND SPACE Marjorie Gorman

Many teachers would not include proof as one of the most important aspects of mathematics to concentrate on at KS1. However, the national curriculum makes it clear that children at KS1 should develop their knowledge and understanding of mathematics through practical activity, exploration and discussion. And it is within this discussion with interested adults that the beginnings of proof lie.

With the introduction of the national numeracy strategy, schools recognised that the three-part lesson would provide opportunities for children to describe and explain their work, but providing practical resources for whole class 'hands on' experience could prove expensive.

I have been working with some KS1 teachers on developing shape and space activities in their infant classes. Building blocks, construction toys and sets of plastic shapes found in most nurseries and reception classes are very useful for an informal exploration of 2D and 3D shape. There is a wide range of material available but most of it has a distinct disadvantage – the shapes included are entirely regular. However, card off cuts and pieces of brightly coloured paper provide a valuable resource that costs next to nothing and includes lots of shapes that are quite irregular. Teachers can use the pieces of card or paper to pose useful questions and help children name and describe many mathematical shapes.

In a quickly gathered collection we found all kinds of shapes and sizes of triangles, pentagons and hexagons which could be displayed in different orientations.

We added a few other shapes and used the collection to play a range of shape games. Children took a shape from a hat and described it, counted the number of sides and gave it a name if they could.

We talked about the different ways of naming shapes, – a tri -angle but pent -agon and hex -agon. We linked the work to literacy activities and asked the children to use different shaped paper for their writing. The aim was to try to make the names more than labels.

I then introduced a giant pack of ATM MATS (Mathematical Activity Tiles) – usually thought to be more appropriate for junior and secondary pupils. They are reasonably priced and, treated with care, they last a long time. The children loved the attractive patterns and the range of colours. The teachers liked the selection of shapes and the large quantities, particularly of the smaller shapes. They were able to plan whole class lessons without worrying whether there would be enough equipment for everyone in the main part of the lesson.

During the next couple of weeks I saw some very interesting and effective lessons on shape and space. The children enjoyed trying out different ideas while the teachers knew they were providing opportunities for children to solve problems and acquire a rich mathematical vocabulary in meaningful situations. From the earliest years the children were encouraged to describe and explain what they were doing. Several lessons were particularly memorable.

Reception

In the reception class, after an introductory exploration of the different shapes available in the MATS pack, we gave the children a quantity of the same shapes to use to make other shapes or pictures as they wished. Some children worked in pairs, but most chose to work on their own. Quite different designs emerged from the tables using the yellow

It is within the discussion with interested adults that the beginnings of proof lie.

From the start, children were recognising these shapes as triangles even when they were 'upside down'.

One child knew he had used hexagons for his design. He made a dinosaur. Another child made a long path of octogons – out of the classroom.

What shapes have you used?

Octogons – they have eight sides – I counted them. An octopus has eight tentacles did you know?

What did you make?

I had a lot of shapes. I wanted to make a long line. I thought it would reach the hall but it didn't.

Why?

Because I didn't have enough shapes.

Y1

Children referred to the different triangles in the pack as the 'yellow'(equilateral) and 'orange' (isosceles) triangles. The challenge was to find out what other shapes they could make using these triangles.

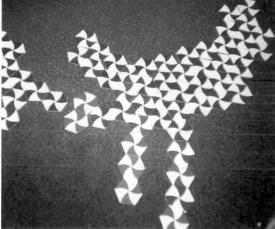

(or equilateral) triangles from those using the orange (or isosceles triangles). From the start, children were recognising these shapes as triangles even when they were 'upside down'.

At the end of the lesson, the teacher asked the children to look at the different work around the classroom. She asked some children to name the shapes they had used and describe their shape or pattern to the rest of the class. The teacher adjusted her questioning to the individual children.

> Well hexagons have six sides and one side of each of the triangles is a side of the hexagon that makes six sides, so it's a hexagon.

What shapes have you used?
What shapes are the spaces?
Tell me about your pattern.
How is it the same as Lisa's?
How is it different?
Mine goes round and round. Hers has diamond spaces.
Why do you think it is different?

Some children quickly grouped the triangles into hexagons.

Teacher asked what shapes they had made. 'Hexagons' came the reply.

How do you know they are hexagons?

I can see six triangles.

Well hexagons have six sides and one side of each of the triangles is a side of the hexagon that makes six sides, so it's a hexagon.

Another group found they could make a hexagon, change it into a larger triangle then into an even larger hexagon.

'Just look at this!' they said 'Isn't it wonderful?'

Y2

During another lesson the challenge was to find out which shapes fitted together without leaving spaces. Some children with 10-sided shapes had to work on the floor but they didn't mind as it gave them the opportunity to spread out the shapes and discover, to their delight that they had some star-shaped spaces. They were so excited. The children with the pentagons got quite frustrated as they kept moving the shapes around to close a gap only to find another gap opened up elsewhere.

'What if you had more yellow triangles?' asked the teacher.

The children thought for a minute.

It would go on and on making triangles and hexagons, triangles and hexagons – through the wall and into the playground. We could cover the world.'
How do you know?
Well why should it stop?

The children with the orange triangles found they could not make hexagons.

Why can't you make hexagons with your triangles?
Because we need more than six of them to meet in the middle.
Look, we can make star shapes and triangles that keep growing.

The teacher asked about the number of smaller triangles in the larger.

How many triangles will there be in the next size triangle?
How do you know?
That's what's happened so far.

Tell me about your pattern. Which shapes are you using?
We are using pentagons
And would you say pentagons fit together without leaving spaces?
Well some of them do. But then, look what happens. We can only get them to fit together with a boat shaped space and diamond space. We can't get them all to fit together without the spaces.
And does that always happen?
It does to us. We could try with more shapes to see what happens then.

All photographs courtesy of Marjorie Gorman and Kay Sewell

Some children asked if they could make some of the shapes into pyramids. I was very apprehensive. Strong glue and young children form a risky combination and there was a new carpet on the floor. I need not have worried – the children followed the rules. They dipped the edges of the tiles briefly in the glue and held them together while they counted to twenty. I must say they were more successful than the teachers on a previous maths course who had not followed the rules, had used far too much glue, which made the tiles soggy and impossible to stick together.

together. They fit together easily when working in 3D. She made a great impression on her classmates by building up a dodecahedron. She was so thrilled by her success she overcame her shyness and described to the rest of the class how she had made this very special shape with the name they all learned very quickly.

Sam (7 years 1 month) and Helen:

S (looking into a beaker with straight sides) How many thingies has a hexagon have?

H 'Thingies'?

S Yes, you know, straight bits.

H Do you mean sides?

S Yes.

H A hexagon has 6 sides.

S (pause, still looking into beaker) Oh. I've got an oxygen.

Most of the children made triangular or square-based pyramids. Some even used pentagons as a base. There was an interesting discussion about different kinds of pyramids.

What do we know about pyramids?

They are in Egypt

How many faces do they have?

Four, five or six

Explain

If they have a triangle base they have four faces, a square base they have five, and a pentagon base has six faces.

One girl was intrigued by the pentagons and needed little encouragement to start to glue them

Sophie spent some time making a pattern with hexagons and equilateral triangles, which she then edged with squares, using a triangle to fit in the corners. See fig.1.

The teacher joined her.

What if you made two rows of squares round your design how many triangles will you need at the corner?

Two, I think. Oh no, look, it takes three.

And what if you made three rows of squares?

I don't want another row of squares.

However she did make a similar pattern later in the week and was interested enough to tell the teacher she used one triangle in the first row, three in the second and needed five in the third row not three as she first thought.

Discussion in all the lessons, both during and at the end of the sessions was meaningful and important to the children who wanted to share with others the interesting things they had learned. Striving to relate their experiences and explain to others helped them to extend their vocabulary and clarify their own thoughts – important foundations for geometric reasoning and the development of proof in later key stages.

Teachers encouraged the discussion, naturally and informally, by providing the relevant vocabulary, sometimes modeling a statement but always by giving the children an opportunity to think about what they had been doing and reflecting on what they had learned. The sort of questions they posed were the how, what, why type of questions that encourage higher levels of thinking.

Marjorie Gorman is a retired teacher and freelance consultant.

Colin Ross

fig 1

ENCOURAGING ALL LEARNERS TO THINK

Liz Bills, Penny Latham and Helen Williams

The authors believe that the way to promote mathematical thinking is by effective questioning. What follows is an attempt to look at how this may be done with A level students (in black type) and Y1 children (in blue type)

1 Reflective questions

When introducing a new topic to a class or demonstrating a technique on an example at A level, I will often ask questions of the class to make sure they are following. These questions may be at very different levels of difficulty, from completing a calculation to giving an overall strategy or justification for the technique.

With an A level class I would tend towards the more taxing type of question. For example, suppose I were working through the following question as an example:

Find the equation of a straight line with gradient 3 which passes through the point (2, 8)

Before starting I might ask
- how do I know that this question has exactly one answer?
  - could we get an answer to it by drawing the line to scale?
    - what do I expect the answer to look like?

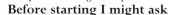

One Y1 activity is to use the OHP, 5 transparent counters and a hiding cup to do some mental calculations.

Before starting I might ask
- How do you know there are 5?
- How can you make us really believe there are 5?

- I am going to hide some counters under the cup – what do you think we are going to be doing next?

During the working I might ask
- what does the family of lines expressed by $y = 3x + c$ look like?
- what should I do next?
- why should I substitute (2, 8) for (x, y) in ?

During the working I always ask
- for predictions and explanations about the number of counters hidden under the cup; 'why do you think there are none hidden, Ben?'

It is important I do not stop at the first 'correct' answer, but instead encourage many children to contribute.
- are you sure? how do you know?

Children may want to change their mind about their answer: 'You don't seem sure about that . . . do you want to have more time to think?' 'Have you changed your mind? – that's fine.'
- we have had some different answers for this one . . . could each one be correct? How do you know that?
- put a picture in your head about what you may see when I pull up this cup

Afterwards I might ask
- summarise the procedure we used in that example
- are there any numbers we could have been given in place of 3 and (2, 8) which would have made the question impossible?

Some of these questions will require considerable thought and I would not necessarily expect an immediate answer. Depending on the difficulty I would either
- tell the class that I was giving them a moment to think about it and then invite responses

- tell them to discuss the question with their neighbour, more than likely needing to write something down, and be prepared to give their answer to the class in two or three minutes.

Afterwards

This is my opportunity to lift children above the task itself. Reflective questions take time to answer, 'Do you want a minute to think? I'll come back to you . . .' Talking to a 'working partner' helps create thinking time.

- how did you know how many were under the cup each time?
- can you tell me how the game worked?
- in your head, plan what you might do when it is your turn/tomorrow

2 Outline solutions

If you use a traditional text book for teaching A level, you will almost certainly find a 'Miscellaneous Exercise' at the end of each chapter. Pupils usually find these more difficult than the exercises on individual techniques.

One strategy is to divide the class into groups and allocate questions from the miscellaneous exercise to each group for them to write an outline solution, that is a solution which explains what to do rather than does it. An example is given below. These outline solutions are then distributed to the rest of the class for their use in working on the exercise.

Question: A circle, radius 2 and centre the origin, cuts the x-axis at A and B and cuts the positive y-axis at C. *Prove* that ∠ACB = 90°.

Student's outline solution:

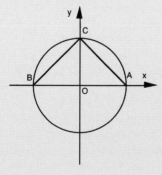

Find the co-ordinates of A, B and C.
Find the lengths of AC and BC. Use Pythagoras' rule to see if $AB^2 = AC^2 + BC^2$. If it is, then angle ACB is 90°.

After a period of time focusing on addition, I want to assess how children's range of strategies are developing:

3 + 4 : I deal with the answer quickly:

- We agree it's 7 – now we're going to talk about how you did it – that's just as important
- Let's find a way to work this out – let's see how many different ways we have.

3 How true?

Some mathematical statements are always true, some are sometimes true and some are never true. In many contexts the question as to which category a statement falls into can be a useful discussion starter.

Example of a possible statement:

$$\frac{1}{a} + \frac{1}{b} = \frac{1}{a + b}$$

Children can be drawn in by comical comparisons:

I show a container of beads; 'How many do you think are inside?' I write up a number that is ridiculous and some possibilities:

- Could there be 3 in here?. . . How about 10 . . . 50 . . . 100?'
  . . . why? . . . why not?
- Would you rather . . . have 1p for each letter of your name OR 20p?

4 Reversals

Many routine exercises in A level mathematics can be turned into something more thought provoking by reversing the task.

For example, instead of asking
find the turning points and points of intersection with the axes for the curve
I could ask
find the equation of a curve which crosses the x axis three times, once at (0, 0), once at (2, 0) and once again, and which passes through the point (2, 3). Is yours the only solution?

Most routine Y1 activities can be turned into something more thought provoking by opening these out. Constraints can be introduced later as 'What ifs':

- I provide 2 circles, a pile of cubes and ask children to generate their own 'sums' (what if. . . you have to use all the cubes each time?).

Young children can be invited to see things from different points of view. I might ask of two similar shapes:

- Tell me something that makes these the same . . . (they are both blue) that makes them different (this one's more pointy)

5 Conflict discussion

New sixth formers often harbour some persistent misconceptions, particularly in the realm of algebraic manipulation, and others may develop as the course progresses. Raising them as an item for discussion may help to dispel conceptions that the pupils did not realise they had.

For example, I might ask pupils to prepare arguments for or against the statement

$$\cos(A + B) = \cos A + \cos B$$

You don't have to think much if everything is as you expect. I could introduce a 'disturbance' for children to make sense of. For example:

- how many things can you fit in this pot? Abdul says he has 500 in his . . . could that be right? What do you think?
- cutting holes in a once-folded sheet of paper: I don't think you can make a square . . .
  Who thinks . . . and who thinks . . .? Why?

One 'disturbance' is a puppet who makes mistakes when counting, such as missing out a number, or counting something twice. The puppet becomes the medium to discuss children's misconceptions about counting. It also shifts the focus from child as learner to child as knowledge holder.

6 Working on an exercise

Text books often present exercises which contain large numbers of questions of a similar type. Pupils might be asked to work through these exercises in order to develop fluency in the particular technique. However such an exercise may be worked *on* as well as being worked *through*. For example the following questions could be asked:

- what do all these questions have in common?
- what makes the later questions harder than the earlier ones?
- how can the questions be categorised?
- put these questions in order of difficulty, giving justifications
- write an easy/hard question of this kind

This makes me think of Y1 children being asked to create many repeating patterns. If we have each worked *through* making a repeating fruit pattern, we could then work *on* these patterns:

- let's find some that are the same as this one: tell us what is the same . . .
- which one is an easy pattern (to make . . . to describe) . . . why?
- which of these is a hard one to carry on? Why do you think that?
- can you make a hard pattern of your own?
- what makes it hard?
- what do you want to try next? why?

7 Particular, peculiar, general

A few years ago I developed a teaching ploy to encourage, amongst other things, practice in expressing generality. The name I gave to this ploy was 'particular, peculiar, general' abbreviated to PPG. First I would ask students to write down, for example 'A particular number which leaves a remainder of 3 when divided by 7'. Typical responses would be 10, 17, 24. Next I would ask for 'A peculiar number which leaves a remainder of 3 when divided by 7'. Here I got responses like 703, 39 826, 7 773, 70 003. Finally 'A general number which leaves a remainder of 3 when divided by 7' solicited responses equivalent to $7x + 3$.

Y1 pattern work can be approached on a surface level or much deeper. Take a repeating line of fruit; O O A O O A . . . I am not expecting all children to be working with the general, some will be just talking about the materials; this is a good start. Others will be able to contrast and describe on a more general level. From: 'Orange, orange, apple . . .'; to: 'That , that, then that . . .' or even: 'Two of those then one of those . . .'

I still ask everyone questions to move from a particular description towards a more general rule:

- what is happening? . . . How do you know that is the next one?
- what if it stretched backwards?
- what if you make this pattern, but with the cubes . . . by clapping and stamping?
- can you make a pattern that goes: this, this, that, this, this, that . . .

Liz Bills teaches at the Institute of Education, University of Warwick; Penny Latham is a mathematics consultant; Helen Williams is a mathematics consultant and edits Mathematics Teaching.

Many of these ideas have been developed from past ATM publications and particularly from the work of John Mason.

FAMILY NUMERACY: BOUND BY THE BSA Jean Millar

Camden Family Numeracy Project
Maths for Parents and Children Under - Five

£ ÷ +
Do you want to help your child with maths at home?
Would you like to improve your own maths too?
X - £
Do you want to understand more about how your child learns maths at school?

LEARN MATHS WITH YOUR CHILD
Come to the new maths classes
run by Jean Millar/contact Maggie

STARTING: Wednesday 13 January
at Thomas Coram Early Childhood Centre
10 - 12 noon
then every Wednesday morning this term
from 10 - 12 noon

TALK TO YOUR CHILD'S TEACHER IF YOU ARE INTERESTED

Small class Good fun Friendly

"Stephen is always counting now – everything, everywhere we go"
"Chloe keeps asking when she can do her maths – she loves playing the games"
"Joseph was very shy when we first came, but now he asks questions more"
"After going on the maths walk, Kamrul keeps asking what door number it is"

This feedback comes from parents of some of the three- and four-year-olds who have been taking part in Camden LEA's family numeracy programme. It is just some of the evidence for the popularity of the programme which has been running since 1997.

As with all pilot projects, those of us involved with Camden's family numeracy programme have had our fair share of challenges. However, the comments above, and other more formal evaluations, suggest that overall the programme has been very successful. From the beginning, great care was taken in the choice of suitable centres and we have been very lucky that staff in the centres have been so totally committed to the programme and to the recruitment of parents. At the same time, the in-service training given to early years' practitioners working alongside the family numeracy consultant

> We are giving parents entitlement to education that they would not have otherwise and opening up opportunities for them to further their interest in their children's learning.

enabled them to quickly absorb the structure of the programme and to lead on it subsequently.

The only London-based pilot project, Camden's family numeracy programme received initial funding from the Basic Skills Agency (BSA) and Camden LEA from September 1997 to March 1998. Further funding from John Lyon's Charity enabled the project to continue to March 1999. Since then, the funding has come from the Standards Fund and the BSA.

Sadly, the BSA has recently announced that it will not be able to fund future courses as 'the programme does not meet its guidelines'. Among the reasons given for this decision were the following:

- the parents involved did not have basic skills needs
- no separate sessions were provided for the children
- the tutor did not have recognised qualifications
- no provision was made for parents to work towards accreditation
- there was no assessment of the participants.

In my view, and that of many in the field, these so-called weaknesses not only misunderstand the nature of good family numeracy teaching but also point to an inherent flaw in the criteria whereby such projects are funded.

We are giving parents entitlement to education that they would not have otherwise and opening up opportunities for them to further their interest in their children's learning.

It is difficult not to agree with the prognosis of the Director of the National Institute of Adult Continuing Education, Alan Tuckett [1]:

> *'Now we hear that only those adult learners who have signed up on courses, and sat and passed an approved qualification in basic skills will count*

CAMDEN FAMILY NUMERACY PROJECT

NUMERACY QUESTIONNAIRE FOR PARENTS

NAME:

NAME OF CHILD:

What do you think about when asked about maths?

What sorts of things do you do with your child at home to help them with maths?

How would you like to help your child more with maths?

What do you feel you need to learn in order to do this?

Would you be able to spend a morning, each week this term, at this school to help you do this?

If you are not able to, what prevents you from doing this? (Young children can join you in the class)

Camden Family Numeracy Project

Evaluation Questionnaire for parents

How useful have the maths classes been to you?

Very useful
Quite useful
Not very useful

Which activities were the most useful or interesting for you?

Which activities were the most useful or interesting for your child?

Have the classes changed the way you help your child at home with maths?

Yes   No

If yes, what sorts of maths activities do you do with your child at home now that you didn't do before?

towards the national target of 750,000. . . We risk letting a tool to measure progress distort what is taught and learned.'

The Camden programme

In defence of the Camden programme and with reference to the BSA's reasons for not continuing funding:

● We were working with a very mixed group of parents, some with basic skills needs, but all needing help with how mathematics is taught in schools

● It is doubtful that good early years practice would support nursery children having an additional, dedicated hour of mathematics

● The tutor was a qualified teacher in the school, known to children and parents

● As for assessment, diagnostic and evaluative questionnaires are issued at the beginning and end of the course. (see top right)

Of course, we did not get everything right during the pilot. However, all those involved gained

invaluable experience and at the same time built the foundations of a secure and potentially thriving provision in an area where it could provide real benefits.

Camden is a socially and culturally mixed inner-London borough, with prosperous Hampstead in the north and the council estates of Summers Town and King's Cross in the south. Each term, two schools or early years centres are chosen for the family numeracy programme. The choice is made on the basis of SATs results for mathematics, the percentage of free school meals and the degree of involvement of parents in school activities. The areas chosen for family numeracy were in King's Cross/Euston and Kentish Town. Both are areas of high social deprivation where families are not normally involved in school activities and whose members, on the whole, have not received further or higher education.

Family Numeracy Spring Term 2002: Session 7
Focus: Shopping/Weight

Activity	Learning Intentions	Differentiation	Resources	Evaluation
Introduction (on carpet) Supermarket shop song Compare the weights of the objects in the song Finding numbers on the packets	To reinforce counting to ten with the song. To encourage re-call and memory skills. To use comparative language of weight (heavier/lighter)	Through questioning: Which is heavier, the cornflakes or sugar? Can you read any numbers on this packet?	Food containers (mixed) Different weight boxes eg Cornflakes, sugar Supermarket song sheet.	Children enjoyed looking at the shopping items and finding numbers. Found heavier/lighter difficult
Activity 1 Role play shop area. Supermarket. Ask children whether they are going to be shopkeepers or customers. Role play choosing items, asking for prices, giving oney and receiving change.	To recognise the coins to 10p To relate money to real experiences To understand exchanging money for goods	Write a shopping list if the child desires. Help child with asking questions: what would you like today? How much money have you got?	Shop items and labels and food containers (as above) Shopkeeper, customer labels Receipt books, clipboards Calculators, felt pens Cash register Baskets, bags, purses Real money(1p,2p,5p,10p)	Shop very successful. K. insisted on writing receipts for everyone and S. had to be persuaded to let others have a turn on the cash register! Beginning to see differences in coins but not values.
Activity 2 Make playdough. Measure out ingredients with children and mix together.	To follow instructions in a recipe. To have experience of measuring quantities	Through questioning: How many cupfuls of flour do we need? What will happen when we add the water?	Plain flour,salt food colouring & oil cream of tartar Bowls, saucepan and rolling pins	S's mum took charge of this activity and helped children with measuring cupfuls.
Activity 3 Shopping List game. In a group, share out trolley cards and spread food cards on the table. Take turns to pick up card and match.	To match pictures and to extend food vocabulary Turn-taking and sharing. Following instructions	Through questioning: What is this called? How many things do you need to find to fill your trolley?	Shopping list game- (Orchard Toys)	F. had borrowed this game in the week so was able to teach other children how to play it.

Parents / Carers
- Discuss activities: give out playdough recipe and supermarket song sheets. Practise the words.
- Discuss ways to help at home: shopping , play shop, empty containers,3D shape words, comparing items (heavy/light)
- Open up empty packets and identify 2D shapes. Turn inside out and remake packet.
- Continue money problems from last week and introduce calculators- take home to complete.
- Discuss exchange rates of different currencies. Bring conversion charts in next week.
- Borrow a game

The pilot model of a two hour weekly workshop in each school seems to be effective.

The structure

The second hour is for parents alone. Here they can discuss the mathematics behind the activities and make games and equipment to help their children at home.

In the first hour, parents and children (from 3 to 5¼ years) participate in mathematical activities together. Assessments carried out at the end of the pilot project revealed that children involved had made significant improvement in their mathematical skills, particularly in counting, reading and writing numbers and using mathematical language in describing shape, space and measures. Their enjoyment of the subject was also enhanced, largely as a result of the games, number rhymes and songs which they sang with their parents.

*Going to buy some food
At the supermarket,
one tin of baked beans,
Put it in the basket.*

*Going to buy some food
At the supermarket,
one tin of baked beans and a bag of rice,
Put them in the basket.*

Teacher: How many items are in the basket now?

*Going to buy some food
At the supermarket,
one tin of baked beans and a bag of rice,
  and a box of eggs,
Put them in the basket.*

Teacher: How many items are in the basket now?

. . . and a loaf of bread . . .
. . . and a carton of milk . . . .

To the tune of *One man went to mow*

We are in the process of monitoring the effects family numeracy has on children's mathematical progress in later years. Children from the pilot year have been tracked by the BSA and the results were very encouraging. Unfortunately, it is only possible to monitor a small percentage of children in this way due to the mobility of the population in inner-London.

The second hour is for parents alone. Here they can discuss the mathematics behind the activities and make games and equipment to help their children at home. Ideas for activities are given each week and parents report back on how they have worked. They are also involved in planning the mathematical topic for the following week and are issued with a folder in which to keep handouts of activities.

Depending on the needs and wishes of the group, we attempt to present adult numeracy in an exciting and stimulating way. A popular aspect of the classes is the home loan system of games which the parents and children borrow each week. Parents report that their other children often join in with the games. This not only reinforces the mathematical concepts but also encourages personal and social aspects of the work in a family setting. Certainly, returned questionnaires revealed that parents had increased the time spent with their children at home on mathematical activities. The games have also been beneficial to the centres as a starting point for a home loan system on a larger scale.

Further developments

A significant proportion of the parents attending the family numeracy courses in Camden is bilingual; some are refugees. Although some of the latter have mathematics qualifications from their own countries, the way they have learned the subject is often very different from the way it is taught and learned in the UK. The classes also offer a social setting for these families where they can meet other parents and discuss educational issues in a supportive and safe environment. Often this leads to an interest in furthering their own education or helping in the school, or centre, as an assistant; about 20% of parents take up further education. However, the value to these adults in terms of confidence building is immeasurable. Family numeracy should be seen as part of the government's overall drive for lifelong learning. Sadly, in its narrow focus on the passing of tests, the BSA seems to have lost sight of this important principle.

Support is being given to schools and nursery centres to continue family numeracy classes. It is hoped that early years practitioners trained on the programme will develop professionally by leading these classes. This year, two courses are being led by a bi-lingual support worker and an early years'

Shopping problems

❖ What is the total of £110, £12, £3.43 and £11.07?

❖ How much does one of each cost?
   10 for 3.90
   100 for £16.00
   5 for £1.55

❖ Find the cost of 145 bottles of lemonade at 21p each. What change do you get from £50?

Things at half price now cost:

£36.18	£111	£27.34	£274.30

What was the original price of each item?

❖ Three people won £363 630 on the lottery to be shared equally between them. How much does each one get?

---

assistant. A centre network is being established to give support to new participants and to enable the exchange of ideas about resources, recruitment and retention.

What we have learned

We have learned, for example, that a good team with clearly delineated responsibilities is essential. Ideally this should comprise an early years practitioner to run the classes, a teacher with adult teaching experience to lead the parent sessions, someone to take responsibility for recruiting and retaining parents and someone to support parents and children for whom English is an additional language. Publicity in English and other languages should be disseminated well in advance and should target all parents – not just those with basic skills needs. Classes should be at convenient times (mornings have been most successful in Camden) and every effort should be made to provide a welcoming atmosphere with a space away from the class to meet and make refreshments. It helps if the crèche has a crèche worker who is known to the parents. All these factors should help create and maintain a group of parents who have the confidence and commitment to attend regularly.

Above all, the emphasis needs to be on how parents can help their children in an unthreatening and motivational way, enjoying mathematics together. Parents want to help their children with mathematics, feel more confident with the subject and learn about how mathematics is taught in schools today. If they want mathematics qualifications or to study mathematics at their own level then an adult numeracy course may be more appropriate.

Funding, of course, is crucial. BSA funding has recently been transferred to the Learning Skills Council (LSC). It is to be hoped that the LSC may be more flexible in its criteria and take a more balanced view of different models of family learning.

We must celebrate the contribution that family numeracy can make to social inclusion and lifelong learning. By stimulating parental interest in what their children do at school we develop positive attitudes towards learning in the whole family.

Jean Millar is a family numeracy consultant for Camden.

> Above all, the emphasis needs to be on how parents can help their children in an unthreatening and motivational way, enjoying mathematics together.

Reference

1 Alan Tuckett, *Times Educational Supplement*, 8 February 2002

Pages originally published in MT